About *Lifeguard Ken Tells All*

For twenty-six summers author Ken Cassie worked as a lifeguard on Atlantic Coast beaches, taking part in one thousand rescues. He has often wondered why some bathers who had trouble managed to reach shore, whereas others had to be rescued. Both groups had little idea of the forces that had impeded their efforts to make it in. Fortunately, professionals alertly watched them.

In recent years, danger in the surf has increased. Larger numbers of people now bathe before and after lifeguard hours, as well as before and after the traditional beach season. Such changes have increased the chances of drowning. The need to understand surf dynamics is greater than ever.

Lifeguard Ken Tells All looks at three components of safer bathing: first, understanding how the ocean works; second, effectively responding to danger; and third, coping with a reflex as dangerous as the ocean—our own panic.

Lifeguard Ken Tells All

Enjoy the Surf. Safely.

Ken Cassie

Shore Thing Press
Archer, Florida

Additional copies of *Lifeguard Ken Tells All* may be ordered at www.lifeguardken.com.

Published by Shore Thing Press
Archer, Florida

International Standard Book Number: 978-0-9987380-0-0

Printed in the United States of America

Dedication

To those bathers who did not make it, but could have, and to those who, with a little knowledge, will.

Acknowledgments

My deepest gratitude to:

Jack Hoban, my cover designer and creator of the iconic "Lifeguard Ken" title, which far outshines the guy it represents. Jack constantly exhorted me to trawl my memory for relevant experiences that I hope enliven an otherwise didactic survival guide.

Gerry, whose wordcraft and talent for constructing a beautiful book provided the best possible platform for what I have to say and, above all, for his tolerance and patience.

Elise, whose perceptiveness and persistence helped me clarify foggy areas that I would have been content to sidestep.

Shelley, my partner in life and love, who has a few cameo scenes in the following pages.

Foreword

The Ocean and Me and You

The Ocean

As a specialist claiming to have something to say about safe ocean swimming, I had better fess up from the start. My first five years on Earth passed in abject terror of the ocean. My dad bore part of the responsibility. Dad was a kind man. But his stance on fear was brusque: "Face it. Overcome it. Move on." He would carry me into the ocean, drop me in the water, monitor my thrashing for few moments, and then snatch me up, blind with terror.

A parenting hard-liner might comment, "Well, you survived, didn't you?" I did, but a method other than Spartan immersions might have succeeded with less torment. I harbor no bitterness at Dad's good old-fashioned aqua training. And if I tactfully omit my screams and thrashing, it makes for an amusing tale.

Immersion training ended traumatically. Not for me, but for my dad. A wave knocked me out of his arms and I cannonballed into the water, tucked in a fetal position. I saw legs and small fish. I bobbed straight back into his arms, and just like that my terror evaporated. Meanwhile, above water, my dad must have been horrified at the thought of losing the apple of his eye. Dad's immersion program had ended suddenly with a neat biblical twist: As ye sow, so shall ye reap. My dad's method had achieved its goal, albeit in an unexpected manner. I was on my way as a water person.

Besides my dad's contribution, I suspect a more instinctual base for my terror. Other bodies of water like brooks, ponds, or the nearby river did not scare me. What was unique about the ocean?

Then it struck me: It was something both intrusive yet generally unnoticed. Noise. I mean NOISE. Even the smallest surf projects an eerily disproportionate sound barrage. It is like a two-ounce house wren with a fog-horn voice. Videos recorded at the beach capture sounds that the subconscious filters out. Later, when viewing the recording, we hear the ocean's full roar faithfully repro-duced. As a child, that roar pierced my sensory filtration system with full force.

The other element is size. I mean SIZE. Unlike conti-nents, the ocean is boundless. In our land environment, we handily compartmentalize most objects. Cars, houses, trains, and people neatly scale down and fit into our mental storage lockers. But building a cubbyhole large enough to contain the ocean is daunting. Even as adults, filtering its size is nearly impossible. So our awe of the ocean and its implied power never leaves us.

Many years ago I was having supper at a lobsterman's home. Beautifully carved around the large oval dining room table were the first two lines of an old Breton prayer:

> *O, God, Thy sea is so great*
> *And my boat is so small.*

This humble prayer, which John F. Kennedy also kept on a plaque on his desk in the Oval Office, perceives a forbidding, mysterious, and vast ocean. The prayer goes on to plead for divine intervention. It sees the ocean as The Great Terrifier. Later in this book we will meet a different face of the ocean, a seductive one that I will call The Great Deceiver.

Me

Both of my grandparents deserve credit for me first seeing the light of day in the Americas. Francesco Cassiere had served four years in the first Italian national army, which, under Giuseppe Garibaldi, had expelled foreign rulers and united the Italian states. But Garibaldi again seized his sword to support his choice for king, Victor Emmanuel.

He also drafted Grandpa Francesco to serve four more years. *"Basta* (Enough)*!"* Grandpa said in effect. "I will go to America, earn a sack of silver, and return to Italy. I will buy land and live like a baron."

After about twelve years the sack was full, and Grandpa prepared to return to *La Patria*, the homeland. Grandma, however, had other thoughts. Until then she had been the obedient spouse. Faced with leaving America, she rebelled for the first and only time, saying "If you go back, you go back alone." Cassiere morphed into Cassie, and my family's roots took hold in America.

My dad brought the ocean into my life. Born in Hell's Kitchen, New York City, he moved to the country at age twelve. To the amusement of his kids, he never lost his Dead End Kids accent ("dem an' doze toikeys," etc.). He did well as an art restorer through the 1920s. In 1929, the year the Great Depression began, in a gem of disastrous timing, he built a bungalow near the ocean.

He liked waves and swam reasonably well. But he disliked sand, wore a seersucker robe at the beach (to my chagrin), always sat under an umbrella, hated the feel of salt on his skin, had no patience for fishing, and got seasick on any body of water. Yet he bought a boat for my older brother. My brother took to the ocean and to boating with a passion. Thanks to him, we never lacked for fish, clams, and crabs.

I was born in the depths of the Great Depression—a "bundle of joy," as my parents put it, tactfully not mentioning the extra mouth they had to feed. My dad was luckier than many. He managed to work two days a week. It was enough to feed and clothe us—but not enough for mortgage payments, which had fallen six months in arrears. We had no hope of catching up.

Enter my dad's only known flaw, aside from dunking. Every year he bought four Irish Sweepstake tickets. His was a tolerable vice, for the Irish Hospitals' Sweepstake raised funds for charitable hospitals in the Old Sod.

At the most critical time he came up with a winning ticket, which provided enough money to save our little shotgun bungalow. Gambling had secured my future near the ocean. I followed in my brother's footsteps, adding a flourish.

I became an ocean lifeguard, a trade I plied for twenty-six summers. When I reached one thousand rescues, I retired. This decision coincided with my retirement from teaching and the opening of my pottery studio. Craft shows now occupied my summer weekends. But the lifeguard within me did not retire.

Even now, certain habits remain when I am at the beach. I feel more at ease when facing the surf. A valuable lifeguard skill is being able to chat while one's eyes independently scan the bathing area. I still do not look

Belmar, New Jersey, lifeguard crew, 1959. Author seated, second from right.

Author launched in surf during lifeguard tournament, early 1970s.

people in the eye as I face the surf. I'm watching the ocean, looking for signs of danger. You'll meet these danger signs in Chapter Two. Adrenaline flows when I see bathers struggling to reach shore, even when lifeguards are alerted.

Over time, my lifeguarding point of view evolved as I watched people enjoying the surf. Better than helping bathers, why can't I help them to help themselves? Gradually I came to believe that ocean bathers can and should more actively manage their own safety in the water.

Author (left) competing in lifeguard tournament, early 1970s.

You

Why do some bathers who are in trouble eventually make it to shore? Why must others be rescued? I saw no conclusive correlation of strength, conditioning, or age between those who could help themselves and those who needed to be rescued. Both groups shared one thing: they had little idea of the forces that had impeded their reaching shore.

Changing times are placing more bathers in harm's way. Many beaches are unprotected. At some beaches, lifeguard crews are understaffed or undertrained. Many experienced lifeguards return to college for fall semesters that start in mid-August, well before the bathing season has ended. As a result, crews may face personnel shortages.

Demographics and costs have made an impact. People are moving permanently to former seasonal resorts, extending the traditional bathing months. Many years ago, in my state, an enterprising town official decided that summer visitors who leave trash on the beaches and who benefit from lifeguard and first aid services should help defray cleanup and safety expenses. Thus began the "beach badge."

Fast-forward to the present. In part because beach fees have grown exponentially, many people bathe after hours, when lifeguards are off duty. These conditions dramatically increase risk in unprotected waters. According to the United States Lifeguard Association, in 2015 bathers drowned seven times more frequently at unprotected beaches.[1]

Finally, more of us vacation abroad in places like Central America, the Caribbean, Hawaii, and, more recently, Southeast Asia. Resorts in these regions do not automatically guarantee competent lifeguards or provide any surf protection at all. These factors, added to sheer population growth, expose more bathers to danger. The need to understand the ocean is greater than ever.

Ken Cassie
March 2017

---

[1] "Statistics," United States Lifesaving Association, *available at* http://arc.usla.org/Statistics/current.asp?Statistics=5 (last visited February 14, 2017).

Introduction

Seduction and Survival

Do you swim in the ocean? Do you visit the beach often or on weekends and vacations? If you ever swim in the ocean, this book can help you and your loved ones bathe in greater safety.

Having traveled extensively, I realized that I could never permanently live away from the ocean. Only recently did I ask myself why. I have admired beautiful areas in the United States and abroad. When the thought of living in one of them arises, the zinger question pops up, only half in jest: "But where's the ocean?" Because the answer has to be moot, I have never heard or asked myself this other question: "Do you like the ocean?" I already knew the answer.

Nor have I ever heard "*Why* do you love the ocean?" That question stops me in my tracks. Well, why *do* I love the ocean? One answer is that once you experience the ocean, the question becomes unnecessary. If a persistent soul demands specifics, I might scrape up a banal bumper-sticker response like "Power and beauty"—which can also describe a muscle car or a youthful Ahnold (think *Conan the Barbarian*). There must be more. Here goes.

Seduction

The ocean embodies freedom. Humans cannot tame it. We make minor adjustments along its fringes, and they are subject to the whim of tropical storms and hurricanes. Were it technically possible, we humans would force the ocean to serve us totally, at whatever cost, as long as we saw a hint of profit in the enterprise. A tragic example is the Aral Sea in Central Asia. The former Soviet Union diverted the Aral Sea's feeder rivers to support farmland irrigation projects. The Aral Sea shrank to a quarter of its former area and is now in its ecological death throes.

If it had been possible, by today humans would have filled in or drained the "empty and useless" Atlantic, Pacific, and other oceans, perhaps leaving some large saltwater lakes for manipulated seafood cultivation. But the oceans—too vast, too deep, and too dynamic—defy human domination.

The ocean liberates me from the dulling strictures of everyday life. No traffic rules, zoning laws, etiquette, noise ordinances, or ubiquitous signs: BRIDGE AHEAD. YOU ARE ON A BRIDGE. YOU HAVE JUST CROSSED A BRIDGE. I got a hint of this release while sitting on the lifeguard stand.

Occasionally I scanned the bathing area with binoculars. A person's face seen close up often revealed a childlike bliss—a momentary release from worldly cares. Sighting a bather with their guard down made me chuckle, but I suspect that a close-up of my face would reveal a similar expression. It is easy to be seduced by beauty and freedom—and perhaps to be less alert to danger.

Survival

Have you ever struggled to reach shore? Did you make it by yourself, or did someone come to your rescue? Do you know what impeded you? Did the experience upset you? "No," you have every right to reply. "It was like eating bonbons. Of course it upset me." Your feelings are understandable. An ocean ambush can both mystify and embarrass. The water appears inviting and safe. You accept that invitation, dive in, and your day turns upside down.

Our familiarity with the ocean lulls us. But each time we enter the ocean we risk dangers undetectable to the untrained eye. In the most literal sense we do not know what we are getting into.

People drown in the ocean both at home and abroad. I state the following categorically: *Most of these tragedies need not happen.* The remedy is simple. No need for Tarot cards or turbaned fortune tellers. Bathers drown mostly for lack of a small and easily acquired body of knowledge. That knowledge is far more vital than whatever physical skills either a lifeguard (professional) or a bather (amateur) may possess.

Granted, lifeguards must swim competently. They must be alert. Above all, for their own safety, as well as for the survival of others, lifeguards must understand how the ocean works. Knowledge is vital to the professional, but the right of ownership is not exclusive to lifeguards. That knowledge can belong to any ocean bather.

You owe it to yourself and those you care about to learn how the ocean works. Think of an everyday activity: for example, when you set off for work. You slide behind the driver's wheel and start the engine. The routine is so ingrained that you think of other things while doing it. You ease onto a major highway at rush hour. "Fine," you say. "What's the big deal? Millions of people do it. What is your point?"

The point is simple: with easily learned skills, you comfortably control that ton of lethal power. Now imagine yourself behind the wheel but you do *not* know how to drive. No rational person takes such a risk. Yet, reasonable people play in the ocean with only the dimmest idea of how this mighty force of nature behaves.

The ocean offers boundless joy. Knowledge ensures that we will keep it that way. To gain that knowledge, we will set three basic tasks: First, understand how the ocean works. Second, respond effectively when problems arise. Third, manage a threat as dangerous as the ocean—our own panic.

Contents

Chapter One

A Lifeguard Drowns

A few years ago, while waiting for a connecting flight in the Cancún airport, a tourist returning home to the United States told me of an incident in which a young man on vacation entered the surf to rescue a young woman in distress. The young woman survived. The young man drowned. The tourist told me that the would-be rescuer had been a lifeguard back home.

I knew of this tragedy only through the tourist's account. Having read no official report of it, I could not swear to accuracy in all details. Would-be citizen rescuers perish every year, but the thought of a lifeguard drowning on a rescue shocked me. How could this be possible?

After twenty-six summers as a lifeguard on the Atlantic seaboard, I could draw some assumptions, even from that sketchy summary. First, the drowning victim had probably been a competent swimmer. Second, he had Red Cross Lifeguard Certification. Third, he was probably in good health. Fourth, he had good intentions.

Fifth, and most pertinent to his tragic death, the victim had been a lifeguard on still water, such as a lake or a pool. He had not been an ocean lifeguard.

You might question my fifth assumption. How can I possibly assert that the young man had not been an ocean lifeguard? Am I an elitist in assuming that ocean lifeguards are better than the rest? No. On the contrary, I consider non-ocean guarding more challenging.[2] But an ocean lifeguard has training and knowledge specific to handling danger in the ocean where it touches the shore.

Armed with that training and knowledge, and with atypical variables aside, the odds are overwhelming that the ocean lifeguard will not drown. My claim rests on the likelihood that the young lady was struggling in an ocean current common to surf everywhere. The ocean lifeguard learns how to deal with this current. In Chapter Two, when we address rip currents, you may find my seemingly brash claim more plausible.

The young man drowned for three reasons. First, he did not know what caused the young lady's distress.

---

[2]Pools, lakes, and rivers provide a different set of challenges for lifeguards, compared to the ocean. First, the water offers less to key on, like a rip, shore break, or thundering surf. Second, bathers are less buoyant. Third, the physiology of drowning is more complex because fresh water in the lungs osmoses oxygen-bearing salt from the blood. Fourth, the lack of variable water conditions may weigh on the non-ocean lifeguard's ability to maintain a high level of alertness. As an ocean lifeguard, I offer these thoughts with empathy and respect.

Second, he did not understand the ocean. Third, he died because he panicked.

The thought that a lifeguard can drown unsettles me. If this can happen, even to one unprepared for surf conditions, then how safe is the average bather, who boasts no special skills or certifications?

On my busy Atlantic Ocean beach, I watched countless bathers struggle in the surf. Most eventually reached shore without assistance. Many were unaware that the ocean had been hindering their progress. They blithely kept paddling. Maybe it was part of their fun. Others, aware of some resistance, kept plugging away and finally reached shore. They seemed to have little idea that a force had been working against them. Nor were they aware of danger before entering the water.

"It Can't Happen to Me:"
Meet The Great Deceiver

Have you or someone you know ever had trouble reaching the shore? Have you witnessed a rescue? No one dreams that this could happen to them. Few of us actually think we will have a fender bender today or catch the flu tomorrow. Forget statistics. Bad stuff happens to the other guy.

The ocean is not the flu or poison ivy. It is the good stuff. Or at least that is how it starts out. When it appears safe and inviting, it enhances our naïve sense of invulnerability. But when most of us enter the ocean, we simply cannot see the lurking danger.

Here is a brief scenario of what could happen to anyone who enters the surf. It is Saturday and a broiling midsummer morning. The temperature has already climbed above 90 degrees. You head for the beach. You need to forget a stressful week. Good things lie ahead today. How can you go wrong with sun, sand, and sea?

You walk across the warm sand. The ocean stretches dreamily to the horizon, glistening in the sun. You spread your blanket and race into the water. Like magic, worries wash away. In the ocean you are as carefree as a child.

You splash about for a while, then roll on your back and gaze into the azure sky. You happen to glance toward shore. Weren't you about fifty feet from the beach? Now it seems that you are a hundred feet away. A moment ago the water was waist deep. Now it is up to your neck. Your toes are lightly bouncing off the bottom. In some recess of your mind a tiny alarm sounds. You swim a couple of strokes to reassure yourself. You try to stand. Now you cannot even touch bottom.

Fear surges through you with a numbing effect. Your mind becomes fixated on a single thought: *I must get to shore.* You swim with all your might. Exhaustion floods your body. You gulp salt water. It nauseates you. Terror chokes you. Signal for help? You cannot raise your leaden arms out of the water. You thrash and struggle. Your world has turned gray.

Fortunately, this story ends well. Having seen your plight, a lifeguard has swum to your aid. But suppose there was no lifeguard? Or suppose the lifeguard's competence matched that of the poor fellow who drowned in Cancún? How would you have fared if survival lay in your hands alone?

To Panic or to Think:
There's the Rub

The option in the title of this section is obvious. Reason beats panic hands down. Here is the catch. With your feet securely planted on terra firma it is easy to say "I'll take reason over panic any day." But if some mysterious force is dragging you away from shore, making that choice may be tricky. When a bather senses overwhelming threat, panic surges as the body's natural, hardwired reaction. The following passage explains the danger of this response:

> The body responds perfectly to an exaggerated message from the mind. It is not the body that needs

fixing. It is our thoughts, our images, and our negative interpretation of our experience that we must correct in order to gain control of panic.[3]

— Dr. Reid Wilson, Ph.D.

Perceived hopelessness unleashes panic in rapid stages. Panic prepares the body for a desperate, possibly hopeless, final struggle. The body starts to close up shop. Specific physiological responses form the last line of defense against perceived doom. Among other reactions, eyes dilate, heart rate increases, and muscles tense. Blood drains from the limbs and pools in the torso. Physiologically, these are normal responses.

Fortunately, for any of us caught in a current near the shore, the key word is *perceived* hopelessness. Consider Mark Twain's familiar quote: "Rumors of my death have been greatly exaggerated." What we must do is modify the *exaggerated*, or false, message that the mind receives. Our job is to insert the correct message. But we face an obstacle.

Changing false input is not easy, especially when the roadblock is our primal fear of drowning. The following is the most recent physiological definition of the drowning process:

---

[3]Dr. Reid Wilson, Ph.D., "Step 2: Understand Your Body's Emergency Response," *HealthyPlace.com*, January 8, 2009 (updated July 27, 2016), *available at* http://www.healthyplace.com/anxiety-panic/articles/understand-your-bodys-emergency-response (last visited February 14, 2017).

Drowning is a process resulting in primary respiratory impairment from submersion/immersion in a liquid medium. Implicit in this definition is that a liquid/air interface is present at the entrance of the victim's airway, preventing the victim from breathing air. The victim may live or die after this process, but whatever the outcome, he or she has been involved in a drowning incident.[4]

— *Circulation*

Even with its impersonal tone, the definition sends a shudder through me, and I dare not ask how it improves upon the previous scientific description. That chill is almost enough to trigger my panic response. That is how touchy and involuntary panic is.

If you have never experienced panic, you may well charge me with exaggeration to dramatize a point. The following anecdote illustrates how easily panic can run roughshod over rational thought.

On a lovely summer afternoon I was taking my turn in our surfboat, patrolling the surf just beyond the bathers. About a half-mile out to sea, a small sailboat was cruising on a gentle swell. It was an elegant, idyllic sight. A few minutes later I looked out to sea again

---

[4]"Recommended Guidelines for Uniform Reporting of Data From Drowning," *Circulation*, November 17, 2003, *available at* http://circ.ahajournals.org/content/108/20/2565 (last visited February 14, 2017).

and saw no sail. Instead, two men were sitting on an overturned hull.

Upon rowing up to them, I asked how I could help. The boat owner opted to stay with the boat and await the Coast Guard. The other man eagerly clambered into the surfboat. As I stand-up rowed us to the beach, the young man sat facing me in the bow seat. He seemed ill at ease. Then he looked down and saw about two inches of water on the bottom. He became more restless. I explained the minor leak. Because the wooden boat sits on the beach more than sixteen hours a day, the seams never seal up.

His eyes began to lose focus. He said, "We're gonna sink." Then he screamed, "WE'RE GONNA SINK!" His eyes widened into marbles, and his skin turned ashen. He looked about wildly, as if preparing to leap somewhere.

I flipped him my hat, which landed in his lap. "You could do some bailing if you feel like it." He started scooping water and flipping it over the side furiously. Gradually he slowed his pace and seemed calmer.

At the time I marveled at a young, robust guy who unravels over two inches of water in a perfectly stable boat. Now I look back on that scene with a fresh appreciation of panic. The hat may have been the key. With it, he saw that he could actually *do* something about his perceived hopeless dilemma. The exaggerated self-talk then dissolved and, along with it, his panic.

Let's summarize by reconnecting a few dots in our strategy to keep panic at bay. On one side we have drowning and our hardwired fear of it. On the other side we have panic as our programmed response. But here is the good news: We can provide ourselves with more accurate input. By inserting the correct dots, we can short-circuit panic. My panicked boat passenger must have done just that. The correct input frees the bather from inappropriate anticipation of morbidity. In street language it means you know you ain't gonna die.

It's time to expel demons. Yes, the ocean is one of the world's majestic wonders. But no inexplicable, supernatural forces lurk there to drag you into its depths. That is the exaggerated message. Those unknowns connect to our fear of drowning and forge a false link between *drown* and *panic*. As we learn more about the ocean and about ourselves, we can strengthen our control over panic.

A World-Class Swimmer?

Early in my lifeguard experience, I thought that competent swimming alone kept you from drowning. Working on a busy beach, I would shake my head at how few good swimmers I saw—less than one percent—maybe five people out of thousands who swam before me in the surf every summer.

It took me years to realize that swimming competence, such as the ability to swim a quarter-mile without
stopping, means far less than knowledge of the ocean.
I do not discount the value of being a decent swimmer.
But on a given day the strongest swimmer in the world
cannot beat a powerful ocean current. On the other
hand, doggie-paddlers who understand their abilities, as
well as ocean conditions, are better equipped to survive.
Smart bathers take what the ocean offers and use it to
their advantage.

The idea that strength and skill may not measure up
is counterintuitive, especially for males. But not this male.
Over the years the ocean has pounded that macho "Ugh,
me stronger than ocean" mentality out of me. So with
full confidence in my "maleness," allow me to introduce a
quaint counterimage: an ocean-savvy grandma. With her
dumpy little putt-putt swimming stroke, she potentially
has a greater chance of survival than a robust eighteen-
year-old freestyle swimmer who does not understand
the ocean. All other things being equal, I place my bet
on Grandma.

You are probably ready to take that bet. But hear me
out. The odds that Granny will not panic come straight
from my childhood. Let's call this little story my little
"grannydote."

I was ten. It was after bathing hours. I was riding
waves on my inflatable surf mat. A young couple about

thirty feet beyond me called out, saying that they could not get in. When I reached them, they threw their arms on my mat. Now the current was drawing me out with them. Although not frightened, I did not know what to do.

Seemingly out of nowhere appeared our angel of mercy. An elderly lady glided up to us, using an almost nondescript mix of sidestroke and breaststroke.

She said, "Well, the pull is not that strong. When the swell comes we paddle, and in between we rest. Nice and easy. Swim with the swell, and rest in the trough." Thanks to that elderly lady, we were soon wading out of the surf. She had used her noodle, not her biceps. And she understood her physical capabilities.

Author, age ten, on the surf mat used in the grannydote rescue.

Oh Yes, He's The Great Deceiver

As a novice lifeguard I first encountered the word *rip*, short for "rip current." Every morning the captain would quiz me on the water conditions. "Is there a rip out there? Show me." At first I could not "spot" a rip. He would point it out and add something like "That's bad water out there. Don't let the bathers near it or you'll have a lot of work."

This novice saw beautiful gradations of greens, rippling textures, and elegant backward whitecaps that seemed to stand still—a glorious sight. The captain saw a threat.

The ocean differs from other hazards in our physical world. The ocean can fool you. But other hazards? Let's see.

You do not touch fire. Fire burns. You know that it will hurt you every time.

As exciting as sky diving and hang gliding may be, their danger is clear: A fall from a great height will kill you with an effective 100 hundred percent probability.

Then we have the ocean: the inviting, exquisitely beautiful ocean, the ocean many of us have "known" all our lives. It can lure us in and suddenly turn on us: The Great Deceiver.

In the following chapters we will examine several ocean hazards, such as along-shore sweep, under-wave turbulence, and, most significant for the bather, the rip current. Then we will work out strategies for dealing with these hazards.

Chapter Two

Exposing Those Demons

I want to define two terms here that appear in later chapters. The first term is BATHER. In part it will refer to either first-time or infrequent visitors to the ocean. It will also refer to people who spend a lot of time at the beach, and who may even be skilled in water sports, but who understand little of how the ocean works. The second term is WATER PERSON. It will refer to lifeguards and water athletes. These people have experience coping with challenging ocean conditions.

Shore Break

A shore break refers to waves that crest and break at the edge of the beach. A two- or three-foot wave that slams down in shallow water or on the sand delivers enormous impact. If you are standing where that little wave rears up, you are at the quintessential wrong place and time. Think of metaphors with breakfast terms, like getting pancaked, waffled, or scrambled. Food for thought aside, a shore break can injure and even kill.

Coping with this danger requires no expertise other than common sense. Do not stand where waves of any size rear up and crunch down on the sand. Even small waves can generate violent impact. Remember the ocean as The Great Deceiver. It lulls you with its exquisite waves, gorgeous color, and … aah … that soft water. It seems to be whispering "You have nothing to fear, Virginia. You are perfectly safe right here (heh, heh). See how shallow it is. How could you possibly get hurt?"

Wrong!

At the critical point of the shore break, the water may be ankle deep. Still, you are inviting injury. Before lifeguards can respond, the wave will have already roughed you up. It may have merely embarrassed you, abraded your skin on the sand, or—worse—injured your spine.

Let's check out prevention. Be attentive even though you may be standing in laughably shallow water. You are in the crunch zone, chatting with a friend. The surf is dancing about somewhere on the periphery of your awareness. Suddenly a wave walls up in front of you. It catches you by surprise. It seems to be looming overhead. You have a nanosecond to react. The following options cannot occur on the spur of the moment. Even if you concoct these options immediately, you may choose the wrong one.

A. Outrun the wave up the beach.
B. Face the wave squarely to challenge it.
C. Stand sideways to reduce impact.
D. Dive through the wave.
E. Do not stand in the danger zone.

The teacher throws in an option B for the guesser. No one wants to invite a solid broadside smash—although it makes a neat challenge for those with testosterone overload or a death wish.

OPTION B ?

Option A is a possibility, assuming that you are able to outrun the wave. Success here depends on too many variables, such as the size and speed of the wave, where you are standing, the softness of the sand, and your own quickness.

Option C is a technique I often use, but there is no guarantee that, depending on the force of the wave, it will not bowl you over. As a rule of thumb, if the wave crest is below hip level I turn sideways.

Option D I would use if the wave is higher than my waist. To a novice, diving through the wave is counterintuitive. The novice's mind retreats from perceived danger, and to dive directly into the danger seems illogical. Yet, option D neutralizes the wave's impact. People with ocean experience feel no qualms about diving through a wave. It is the experienced beach person's choice.

More questions arise. What kind of waves are following the one you just dove through? How much experience do you have? Might you have difficulty clambering back up the beach? Is it suddenly too deep for you? Will you have leapt into a "groin"—a strong but short current pulling away from the beach?

Given the many variations added to the five options, the wisest and simplest is option E. Stand far enough up the beach to be safe from the shore break. Then you can chat away with your friend in safety. Never be forgetful of even the gentlest surf. And above all, face the ocean. The following is an example of why you should.

One of my buddies described this ocean rescue. A teenage girl was standing at the water's edge with her back to the surf. A large wave broke squarely on her back, and the foam engulfed her. My buddy raced up and found her facedown in a foot of water. He placed the unconscious girl on dry sand. She was not breathing. Following CPR procedure, he checked her air passage and found a wad of chewing gum lodged in the back of her throat. When he removed it, the girl quickly recovered. She could have avoided this near tragedy had she had been facing the surf.

A shore break is also dangerous to those playing in it. As an eleven-year-old I paid a dear price. I rode a mat on a wave that slammed me on the sand. My spine bent back sharply, and I blacked out. The lifeguard was standing less than fifty feet from me. He did not respond. Either he did not see me, or he thought I was playing. I regained consciousness quickly and without, it appears, lasting brain damage. But I still carry a mildly herniated disc as a memento.

Highly skilled athletes ride shore breaks. They may use surfboards or bodyboards, or they simply bodysurf. For a few thrilling seconds they channel the shore break at the peak of its power into a speedy vehicle. I do not recommend this hazardous game for the inexperienced, the faint of heart, or those without a death wish.

Beware. Most of us underestimate the danger of a shore break. Maybe the proximity of terra firma falsely reassures the unwary. Shore breaks especially threaten little children, older people, and inexperienced visitors. If you must stand or play near a shore break, do not ignore the potential danger. Be alert and face the water.

Backwash

A person can be strolling along the sandy slope at the water's edge and not perceive this danger. Backwash, or backrush, refers to water from a spent wave. The wave has broken. Its white water has rushed onto and up the sloping sand. Some water from the spent wave sinks into the sand. If enough water remains, and if the slope is steep enough, the water rushes back into the surf.

A large enough wave, a steep enough sandy slope, and a large amount of water can drag unwary bathers down the slope and into the ocean. There, a snarling shore break may await them. The backwash can be strong enough to form a backward wave that carries well out to sea before it dissipates.

As with a shore break, the call word is alertness. Know exactly where you are. Assess surf conditions. All of this may strike you as clinical and perfunctory. But backwash can be deadly to people who think they are safe because they are at the water's edge. In Chapter Four I relate a near-fatal collision with a mountainous backwash almost four hundred feet from shore.

Along-Shore Sweep

Along-shore sweeps occur when waves and a strong wind move in the same direction along the shore. Jetties slow the momentum of along-shore sweeps. Where no barriers jut into the ocean, the sweep will be of greater force.

Another type of sweep occurs in bays. On both sides of these water bodies, currents flow toward the bays as a standard phenomenon. The along-shore sweep may be more frustrating than dangerous. But with the ocean, expect the unexpected.

ALONg SHORE SWEEP

You may find yourself drifting rapidly along the beach, away from your point of entry. It is tempting to swim back. I have watched countless bathers frustrate and exhaust themselves in this futile tactic. They swim and swim and make little or no progress. Others try to wade against the sweep. The solution? It is far easier to get out of the water and walk along the beach to your entry point.

DON'T SWIM, WALK

Let's summarize the first three terms: shore break, backwash, and sweep.

The shore break is the nemesis of novice beach-goers, little children, and elderly people who are lulled by shallow water and nearby dry sand. The shore break can embarrass, bruise or break bones, cripple, or kill.

Backwash can surprise anyone near the water's edge by the simple fact that it comes from the opposite direction of the ocean. If the backwash is strong enough, it can knock a bather down and carry them into the surf.

The sweep can combine with other conditions. If the sweep is powerful and the water deep enough to inhibit walking, a life-threatening danger can arise. The sweep may pass over jagged underwater hazards. Or worse, it might draw you into a potentially deadly rip current or under-wave turbulence.

Under-Wave Turbulence

Under-wave turbulence—sometimes incorrectly called "undertow"—can be lethal. Those vulnerable folks who idle about or play near the shore break will generally avoid under-wave turbulence. At first glance, this thought appears contradictory.

Where there is under-wave turbulence there are large, intimidating waves. This is a case where the ocean is not The Great Deceiver; it is more like The Great Terrifier of the Breton prayer. Massive, noisy surf clearly alerts bathers to danger. It is an easy call to stay out of the water.

I live about a half-mile from the beach. Occasionally the roar of waves awakens me at night. The ocean is announcing the next day's surf conditions. No mystery here. Few of us take monster waves lightly. Noise and size convince us that what we see is what we'll get. Here, the ocean joins fire and altitude as obvious dangers. So we sensibly sit out this water session.

We lifeguards avoided the term "undertow." In our local jargon, anyone who used it did not "know the water." Bathers had fuzzy notions about an unseeable danger out there. Some even believed the scary, and incorrect, literal interpretation of being *towed under*. I've heard it used to describe rip currents as well as under-wave turbulence. Either way, it's an inaccurate and incorrect term. Its gradual disappearance from popular usage is fine with me.

Then a thought struck me. I do not recall my surf buddies or me, with all our surf experience, using any expression to denote water turbulence beneath crashed waves. I came up with the term *under-wave turbulence*. It doesn't roll off the tongue as smoothly, nor does it fit as easily on a sign. But it is spot-on descriptive and hard to misinterpret.

Even in heavy surf no "towing under" occurs. Here is a quick sketch of what does happen. You are in the surf. A huge wave has just crashed in front of you. Two options arise: Stay on the surface and be bashed, or dive. You choose the latter. Of your own free will, you dive to avoid a freight train of white water.

Reason serves you well if it leads you to avoid heavy surf in the first place. Should you find yourself in heavy surf, option one is a bad choice. But option two, diving under the wave, does not guarantee survival. You may find yourself tossed about like a rag doll in Mother Nature's washing machine. That comic image should not mask the reality. As we will see in Chapter Four, under-wave turbulence can kill even an experienced water person, whether surfboarder, bodyboarder, bodysurfer, swimmer—or lifeguard.

WASHING MACHINE EFFECT

Surfers who challenge big waves must contend with potentially lethal under-wave turbulence. They risk it if they have to paddle out to their takeoff point through the area where the waves crash, or if they wipe out while riding their board.

I recently watched a televised big-wave surfing competition at Waimea Bay on the famous North Shore of Oahu, Hawaii. The waves were twenty to thirty feet high. The camera scanned the competitors as they waited their turn to enter the water. Then the camera closed in on the faces of the most experienced and competent water people in the world: big-wave surfers. Each face showed fear.

Unlike panic, fear is an appropriate reaction to the danger of a large wave. Also unlike panic, fear still allows one the capacity for problem solving. Those surfers knew the danger as well as their own physical limits. The margin of survival between the two is not easily calculated. Only after the fact does one learn whether a margin existed. Big-wave surfers absolutely need one condition to survive under a giant wave: having enough air in their lungs.

During this particular surfing contest at Waimea, a monstrous wave suddenly crashed ("closed out") on one of the Hawaiian surfers paddling out. A mountain of raging white water enveloped him. He disappeared as if nature had tapped the delete button. The camera panned the area. A timer popped up in the upper right corner of the screen. Eighteen seconds passed. At last the exhausted surfer popped to the surface. He had just survived under-wave turbulence.

Eighteen seconds seem insignificant. But if you are being thrashed about underwater, unable to control your body, torn this way and that, a third of a minute can be an eternity. Time passes with agonizing slowness. Right now, hold your breath. Count to eighteen: *one-thousand-one, one-thousand-two,* et cetera. It seems easy. Secure in a comfortable chair, you have the luxury of opting out of the exercise when you feel pain. Twelve seconds. Twenty-eight seconds. You also know that you can resume breathing when you choose. The surfer beneath that wave had no idea of when or how his ordeal would end.

Now let us entertain a similar scenario, one that I have lived too many times. Imagine that you are trying to swim out past fifteen-foot waves. Before you get past the break, a set of monstrous waves rolls in. To use a surfing term, you are now *caught inside*, between the wave break and land. Huge waves bear down on you. The first wave crashes about thirty feet ahead of you. Your options: get bashed or dive under. The choice is simple.

Dive. You try to reach the bottom, about ten feet down. If you can touch the bottom you will know which way is up. The wave flings you about like a sneaker tumbling in the wash. The first wave finally passes, releasing its grip long enough for you to push upward and burst to the surface. You gasp for air. Another wall of white water instantly bears down. Before you can draw a full breath, you dive again. The under-wave turbulence wrenches you about without mercy. Lungs ache. Finally you pop to the surface. You really need a full, deep breath before the next wave rolls over you. You look seaward.

Here comes the biggest wave yet—a wall of white water tumbling toward you. Barely sucking in some air, you dive under for the third time. The under-wave turbulence tumbles you so violently that you lose your sense of direction. Which way is up? Energy seeps from your body. You ache. You try to remain calm, aware that struggle is useless. Panic will deplete your precious supply of air all the quicker.

Under-wave turbulence challenges us in an elemental, merciless way. You do everything correctly. You try not to struggle, and you resist panic. You are well conditioned. You are a good swimmer. But if the turbulence outlasts your air supply, you drown. It may slam you into coral, rock, or sand. It can knock you out or break your neck. Against brutish under-wave turbulence, conditioning and courage are worthless.

Experience can help. I do not ooze confidence here because you cannot predict the two main variables: your lung capacity and the might of the wave. I will lay out a survival strategy in Chapter Four. The only testimonial for that strategy is that I am alive to discuss it.

For the average bather I would roughly classify a big wave as one with a face higher than five feet, or about one's own height. Big-wave riders who challenge mountains of water higher than thirty feet surely scoff at my definition. If you dive under a wave smaller than five feet you can probably make it back to the surface when you choose, without undo exertion.

Under-wave turbulence is more the potential killer of experienced water people than bathers. A huge comber deceives no one. People not even close to facing the challenge have the good sense to stay out. Remember all that NOISE and SIZE? Even when viewed from hundreds of yards away, a fifteen-foot wave exudes menace. It is massive. It is fast. It is incredibly loud. The ground trembles. Like cliff diving in Acapulco or a blazing wildfire, the danger of a big wave is obvious.

Here is a final thought on the **U** word. One day while walking a beach on Oahu, I spotted a posted sign: DANGEROUS UNDERTOW. I was speechless. Here was a dangerously misleading word being using by water-savvy Hawaiians! The only sense I could make of the sign was that, given the heavy surf confronting me, it referred to turbulence beneath large, crashing waves.

My first thought was that if Hawaiians can use the term "undertow," why not anyone? We easily sidestep the literal meaning of other words and phrases. Tall buildings don't really scrape the sky. Nitpickers don't really fool around with parasitic bugs. And rip currents don't really tear anything or anyone. Still, something unsettling in the literal and connotative baggage of "undertow" sets it apart.

Unlike other metaphors, being "towed under" touches a subliminal fear of unknown forces. That is the connotative part. Worse, in its literal sense, "undertow" defines a terrifying force that does not exist. With respect to the tacit Hawaiian testimonial, my old lifeguard's aversion prevails. I deny "undertow" access to my working vocabulary.

I also suspect that in Hawaii a large number of water people enter big surf. As long as authorities, water people, and bathers all read the same meaning into a term, I suppose it works. But not for me.

Whatever we call it, under-wave turbulence exists, and we need to recognize it as a major safety menace.

Rip Current

The major threat to the bather is the rip current. The vast majority of drownings occur when bathers find themselves in rips. This is sadly ironic. Unlike under-wave turbulence, the rip is not inherently deadly. We have to find out why bathers drown in rips.

My venerable lifeguard captain occasionally called the rip a *sepus*, a Native American term for tide or current. *Rip tide*, an inaccurate term I hear from bathers, confuses two distinct phenomena of ocean water movement: Waves cause rips. Lunar gravity causes tides.

Tides change with such regularity that charts can predict them. Only where tidal water flows through a narrow passage, like an inlet or river, can it resemble a current. Tides change directional flow roughly every six hours. Tides rise and fall or, as some say, go in and out.

By contrast, rips occur near shore and generally flow away from it. Unlike tides, no chart can predict a rip. Its direction, course, length, width, force, and presence on any given day depend on waves, depth, and configuration of the bottom.

A rip emerges from water pressure that builds up near the beach. One after the other, waves break on the shore, often arriving in sets of up to six. To equalize the pressure, water flows outward in an area offering the least resistance. The stream reaches deeper water and dissipates. This stream within the ocean is the rip.

A rip can be as narrow as a few feet or as wide as a hundred feet. It can be as gentle as a raindrop trickling down your driveway, or it can deliver the awesome surge of a mountain cataract. One minute it can overwhelm, and within seconds it can just disappear. Then it can reemerge. It can stretch a mere thirty feet or a quarter-mile or more out to sea. If the ocean bottom is hard, the rip will follow a consistent course from day to day. With a shifting sand bottom, the rip tends to shift.

RIP CURRENTS
Break the Grip of the Rip!®

ESCAPE · ESCAPE · ESCAPE · ESCAPE

CURRENT · RIP CURRENT · CURRENT

Rip currents are powerful currents of water moving away from shore.
They can sweep even the strongest swimmer out to sea.

IF CAUGHT IN A RIP CURRENT

◆ **Don't fight the current**
◆ **Swim out of the current, then to shore**
◆ **If you can't escape, float or tread water**
◆ **If you need help, call or wave for assistance**

SAFETY

◆ **Know how to swim**
◆ **Never swim alone**
◆ **If in doubt, don't go out**

More information about rip
currents can be found at the
following web sites:

www.ripcurrents.noaa.gov
www.usla.org

*This rip current sign is displayed at beach locations in coastal regions.
Note that there is no mention of panic.*

Viewed from the sky, a rip often resembles a mushroom, with the cap farthest out to sea. At the edges of the mushroom's cap, the rip dissipates. From this angle a rip is most visible. Sadly, this is an unlikely vantage point for a bather.

Classic Rip Configuration

The closer you get to eye level with the water, the harder it is to identify rips. They elude the untrained eye. A bather would sometimes ask me, "Why can't I swim in the spot right in front of my blanket?" I would explain about the rip there. "You ripped what?"

I explain a rip and point to it. The bather peers dubiously out over the water, squints at me as if I have three eyes, and walks off convinced that I am either pulling his leg or batty. Had I announced that great white sharks were right offshore, feeding on Mafia victims, my explanation might seem more plausible. Today, with the media attention given to rips, the bather may be more receptive.

If the rip is so changeable and difficult for a nonprofessional to spot, then how can you identify it? There are indicators. Jetties or any point of land that extends into the ocean often have rips running along them, generally on the windward side. There may be a gap between the jetty and the beach. In that case the current from the windward side will flow through the gap, or cut, and the rip will move seaward on the leeward side.

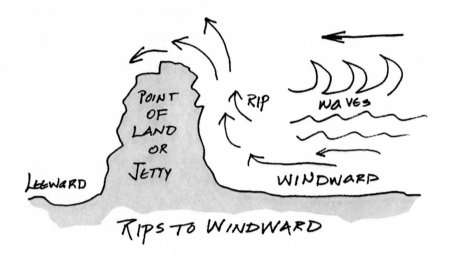

Another indicator is a shallow, gradually sloping bottom. Given this topography, water pressure near shore builds up more readily. And although many bathers prefer low tide, most are unaware that shallow water often increases the chances for the formation of a rip.

If you see waves, suspect a rip in the vicinity. Even in small surf, rips can be powerful. One of the most challenging rescues I took part in occurred on a day when the waves were oversized ripples.

It was a busy weekend. I was due for a break. Before heading off for my cup of coffee, I glanced back at the water. The surface of one bathing area showed an oddly stationary and ruffled texture, like a small shag rug on a hardwood floor. In and around this area were about a hundred bathers.

I decided to swim out in a relaxed way to inspect this odd-looking area. No sooner did I reach the "shag rug" when a powerful rip appeared. The rip suddenly swept out more than twenty bathers. The outward pull was so sudden and obvious that they began to swim furiously, en masse, as if they were attempting a synchronized swimming routine.

In the midst of these thrashing bathers I quickly secured three children most at risk. By the time other lifeguards swam out, the rip had drawn the whole group of us more than a hundred feet from our starting point. In the final count, we rescued twenty-two people from that "funny-looking" water. The Great Deceiver had done its work.

This rescue offers a sound lesson about the ocean. Be alert for the unexpected. This is a fundamental safety mantra for anyone, amateur or professional, who enters any body of water—but especially the ocean.

It takes practice to recognize a rip. Waves and shallow water near the beach are easily seen markers. Study the color and texture of the water's surface. The rip reveals a rougher texture than the water around it. Often, the stronger the rip, the coarser the surface. You may see whitecaps that seem stationary. They may be slowly moving backward, against the wave direction. A strong rip can resemble white-water rapids rushing away from the shore.

As for color, bright sunshine helps you distinguish a rip. If the bottom is sandy—as are most bathing beaches—the color of the rip may be lighter, more yellow-green. If the sun angle is behind you, the contrast may be less obvious. (Light-green polarized sunglasses enhance this color contrast.) Or the color of the rip may not differ.

Let us review the markers for rips:

A. Presence of waves
B. Gradually tapering bottom
C. Different water color
D. Different water texture

You do not need an advanced degree to understand this. You do need practice. When at the beach, sit down on the berm. On this seated drill, check for a correlation between tides and rips. For example, my beach rips ran strongest at low tides, especially at the turn of the ebb tide. Ironically, because the water was shallower, many bathers felt safer.

It is harder to recognize a rip when you are in it. For this reason, scan the ocean carefully before you enter the water. Having done that, there may well not be a rip when you check from the beach. Then you jump in, and the rip starts. I cannot overstate the fickleness of the ocean and your need to be alert.

Before you enter the ocean make a mental note of your position. (All this alertness need not diminish your fun but, rather, can be part of it.) Next, get your bearings. Estimate your distance from shore and your position along the shore. This is easier if you can select reference points. For distance, line up three points, with you as the last one. For example, you are point A. The blue and green umbrella is point B. The water tower in the distance is point C. You now have a point of reference to monitor your distance from the beach.

For your along-shore position, pick a point on land, like an umbrella, building, jetty, navigational marker, or pier. You are the second point. A noticeable change in your position should alert you. For example, if you can now see a side of a house where previously you saw only the façade, you know that your position has changed.

You may not have any point of reference at your beach. That's not necessarily a cause for concern. For all of these positional points, the easiest indicator is water depth. If one moment you are waist deep and the next moment you are standing on your tiptoes, with no propulsion on your part, ask yourself why.

Sometimes you can make direct headway against a rip. Other times the rip is too strong. The critical factor is not the rip—it is *you*. Uncoordinated, harried struggle wastes energy. Worse than that, anxiety-ridden struggle is a split second away from panic.

Posted at many beach entrances are signs, similar to the rip-current sign illustrated on page 32. They may not stress that the rip does not drag you under. Also, those signs do not cite panic as the prime ingredient for drowning. Even if the sign mentions it, just cautioning you against panic is next to useless. It reminds me of the political candidate whose major weapon of his war on drugs was "Just Don't Do It!" I'll bet addicts throughout the land were dancing in the streets, crying "Hallelujah! We are saved!" Words do not help. Tactics do.

In this chapter we viewed five bathing hazards: shore break, backwash, along-shore sweep, under-wave turbulence, and rip current. In the next chapter we plan how to survive the most common threat to bathers: the rip.

Chapter Three

In a Rip?

We have debunked the demons, explored the misleading term "undertow," exposed the dangers of panic, and examined ocean hazards that threaten both bathers and water people.

As we saw, a rip often suggests a mushroom shape, with its crown aimed seaward. With practice you will be able to spot it from shore. The situation differs if you are in the water. You may actually be in a rip and not see it.

It is time to play "What if?" You are swimming and swimming, yet making no headway toward shore. Your first deduction should be that a rip is pulling you away from shore. You are starting to tire. What to do? Answer: Work out a plan.

First, save energy. Stop swimming. Tread water lightly. If that takes too much effort, try floating on your back with your chin toward the sky. If your legs are as spindly as mine, they will slowly sink. Do not worry. Take an easy, deep breath to fill your lungs. Make sure your stomach expands when you inhale. With lungs inflated, the stomach pops out of the water. Even if your toes sink, the rest of you is buoyant. Now, start thinking.

Review the facts. You wanted to go for a dip. You scanned the ocean for rips. You judiciously chose to bathe where you saw none. So a rip must have started up after you entered the water. Remember, you are still floating on your back in the rip. You are in control, so do not panic. I will be right out with the rest of your survival strategy. First it is true confession time.

To dramatize the importance of thinking out your problem in a rip, let's look at a moment from my first year as a lifeguard, when I took a long swim with a pal. We swam along the beach about three hundred feet out. My buddy finished up and turned toward shore. I swam a few feet farther, then also turned toward shore. Suddenly a realization struck me like a mallet blow to my head. I could not make headway. The humiliation of a lifeguard who cannot get to shore overwhelmed me.

Did I pause to assess the situation and then act accordingly? Nope. Did I panic? You betcha. The loud-speaker in my panic-stricken mind blared, "YOU ARE NOT GOING TO MAKE IT, TURKEY! The demon of the deep has you. Hahahaha!" (maniacal laughter). Fortunately, at least for my self-esteem, a conveniently large wave appeared like cavalry to the rescue, and I rode it through the rip to the beach.

My predicament astounded me. Panic had gripped me so unexpectedly and so easily. After all, I did know the water. How difficult was it to figure out that I had swum into a rip? That experience taught me two lessons. First, never underestimate the ocean. Second, be on guard to combat panic. Panic can flare up as spontaneously as a brush fire in a drought. It lurks just below the conscious level. When it tries to pull a palace coup on your mind, you must smother it.

"Hurry up with that survival plan," you grumble. "My fingers look like prunes." Okay, let's sum up:

1. STAY CALM. No octopus is clamping its suction cups on you. No giant clam clutches your ankle. Nothing is towing you under. Calmness is vital to survival.

2. ASSESS THE SITUATION. Yes, you are indeed in a rip. How far out does it go? How powerful is it? If you swim with the swells and rest in the troughs, can you make headway? Is the rip easing up so that you can come straight to shore? Should you swim parallel to shore, then turn to shore? Can you discern which edge of the rip is closest to you?

3. ASSESS YOURSELF. Have your efforts exhausted you? You may have swum too hard before realizing you are in a rip. Make sure not to struggle. Stay relaxed. Float until you restore your energy. If you rest, the rip may take you even farther out to sea. But it may be a good trade for getting your wind back. It is your call, your body. Just do not rush things.

4. FORM A PLAN BASED ON THE PRECEDING INPUT.

With your plan in place, set a simple routine, something like swimming five strokes and resting twenty seconds. Pick your route. Exert yourself within your limits. Just having a plan will by itself boost your morale.

This reminds me of a time when I was completely out of my element, in the mountains. A mountaineer friend had invited me on a climb. From that humbling experience, I recall the infantile routine that oxygen-thin air forced upon me. Imagine: ten baby steps, thirty seconds rest, repeated again and again. Pressing upward, I eventually reached the crest, where my friend lounged in dapper fashion, a cigarette dangling from his mouth.

You might try something like five counts of swim and ten counts of rest. Whatever fits your capacity is fine. Another benefit with this plan: As simplistic as counting to five and to ten may appear, it helps lock your mind in thinking mode and keeps panic at bay.

Oh boy, I can tell all this floating bugs you. What? You have a request? Of course, I reply expansively. Anything you want. Yes, I do know that you want to get to shore. No, I am not going to have you float out here all day. Go ahead, be my guest. Start swimming. Incidentally, which way do you intend to swim? No, I am not being flippant.

Were this real life, you have already tried plan A, and it failed. That is the swim-straight-in plan. Check the next alternative. (No, plan B is not to swim to the shipping lanes and flag down a freighter.)

Slowly, always conserving your energy, always maintaining physical and mental control, swim PARALLEL TO SHORE. You are taking the easiest path out of the rip. You ask which way: right or left? If you can see the rip, swim beyond the closest edge. If you cannot discern the edges of the rip, then go with the wind if it is blowing parallel to the beach. If not, and if there is an along-shore sweep, then go in that direction. Pick the route of least resistance.

Swim about thirty feet, and test whether you can now make headway toward shore. Do not rush. Conserving energy is more important than speed. Instead of the regal crawl, elegant backstroke, absurdly inefficient breaststroke, or show-off butterfly, I recommend the simple sidestroke.

"Surely you jest. My grandmother uses that stroke."

That is exactly my point. Grandma knows what she is doing. Remember the grannydote and the nondescript stroke? Style points do not count. The sidestroke is easy to learn. You can glide effortlessly on either side with a minimal loss of energy. The sidestroke is the closest you can get to resting as you move. Because your face is always out of the water, you have good visibility and you breathe as you wish. Swim with the swells, and rest in the troughs. Morale soars when the ocean helps out.

The key word of step four is *simplicity.* Easiest is best. So let me simplify. If you cannot or do not want to figure out wind direction, strength of the rip, et cetera, then SWIM EASILY PARALLEL TO THE BEACH UNTIL YOU EXIT THE RIP, THEN COME TO SHORE. It is that simple. Didn't I tell you? Let's review salient points.

A. Stay calm.
B. Assess conditions.
C. Assess yourself.
D. Swim easily parallel to shore.
E. When free of rip, come to shore.

Some experts suggest swimming at a 45-degree angle to the beach. In powerful rips, swimming at that angle might sap too much energy. You might try a less acute angle. Use your judgment.

A check for sweeps and rips before entering the water stows data in your memory bank on which to base a plan. Forehand knowledge hedges against surprise and panic.

One bather who had graduated beyond the demonology stage offered the following solution. Let the rip take you away from shore. Do not fight it. When the rip finally peters out, come on in. That's not necessarily a bad solution, and it beats believing in six-headed monsters. The plan starts well enough. But it does not clarify *how* you get in. Do you swim straight in against the rip? The rip may extend a quarter-mile or more out to sea. You would face a long swim against the same current that brought you out there. You also face greater mental stress. The total energy drain far exceeds immediately swimming parallel to shore.

Going out to sea reminds me of a colorful rescue I once made. I swam up to a young lady who was bathing about fifty feet from shore. By the time I reached her with my buoy (which we called *torps*, short for "torpedo buoy"), the rip had washed us more than two hundred feet farther from shore. The rip became ferocious. It was now over a hundred feet wide and ran over a quarter-mile to sea.

On the beach the crew had connected two six-hundred-foot rescue lines. The plan was to tow us in. A lifeguard swam out toward me towing the twelve-hundred-foot line. Unfortunately, he came up about a hundred feet short. The moral of this story is. . . .

"Hold it," you interject. "What happened to the girl?"

Oh yes, I quite forgot about the girl.

Well, a party fishing boat on its way to the marina happened on the scene. Having received her permission, I helped the young lady onboard, and the boat took her back to the dock. Presumably. The fishermen seemed like nice people, perhaps a bit eccentric as I now recall. The eye patches, the peg legs, the nutty parrot squawking "pieces of eight, pieces of eight. . . ."

All right, I will get serious. It's time for you to stop floating and start sidestroking your way in. Gosh, your fingers do look like prunes.

Chapter Four

The Devil in the Not-So-Deep Blue Sea

Talk about your potential killer—under-wave turbulence is the real deal. A rip may pull away from shore and set careless or ignorant bathers up for disaster should they panic. Essentially, a rip is merely a stream that can move you to a place not of your choosing. Your air supply remains secure. You are on the surface. The major challenge in a rip is mental discipline.

Under-wave turbulence can kill you in a couple of ways. It acts like a giant washing machine. It can drown you; drive your surfboard, kayak, or paddle into your skull; or bash you against the bottom. If you are thrust into coral, you can suffer lacerations (think of yourself as an all-meat patty), with attendant infections. Impact can break limbs. I have been stunned a few times when my head hit bottom ("Ha," you say. "All is clear now.").

Why a non–water person would venture into roaring, pounding, hissing, crashing, earth-shaking surf is hard to grasp. We are talking judgment clouded by substance abuse, showing off, masochism, or a death wish. Under-wave turbulence menaces everyone.

A rip can operate in an idyllic, serene setting. This is how The Great Deceiver can fool you. Under-wave turbulence comes in a breathtaking package labeled The Great Terrifier. Large crashing waves and the turbulence beneath them, with their deadly ferocity, are deadly honest. They roar: WE CAN AND WILL KILL YOU.

In Under-Wave Turbulence?

I remind you of my confidence deficiency in suggesting how to cope with under-wave turbulence. Unlike a rip-current situation, in under-wave turbulence the wild cards of lung capacity and the power of any given wave are unpredictable. Here is my best shot, solely based on my experience.

When you are under a big wave, follow this rule: NO STRUGGLING. Or I should say *try* not to struggle. I find it almost impossible. When turbulence pulls limbs, head, and torso in every direction imaginable, the distinction between merely controlling your body and struggling to keep all the parts in place blurs. I instinctively want to fight against the washing-machine effect. Despite my intentions not to struggle, after popping up from a particularly abusive wave, I sometimes feel surprisingly exhausted and have to assume that I must have been struggling. The instinct to regain control over my body contradicts the NO STRUGGLE rule. We will soon examine the absolutely vital part of our anatomy that we must control.

I recall some under-wave turbulence episodes with a shudder. Literally the hard way, I learned how to best cope with the sneaker-in-the-washing-machine syndrome. Let me sketch a composite under-wave scenario. The massive foamy white wall of a crashed wave is bearing down on you. Time your dive. Do not go under too soon. Why hold your breath longer than necessary? If you wait too long, the wave will blast you. Inhale a huge breath of air. Fill your lungs, expanding both chest and stomach. Dive.

Try to reach bottom. Knowing where the bottom is gives a point of reference to locate the surface. This sounds obvious. But turbulence can quickly disorient you. If the action is not too violent, I clutch the bottom in a kind of sprinter's starting position. The bottom also offers a firm base from which your legs can propel you upward. These tactics work—if you can get enough control over your body. A certain level of physical conditioning will serve you well.

Here is that absolutely vital bit of body control: DO NOT STRAIGHTEN YOUR BACK, and DO NOT BEND BACKWARD. This is critical. When my body has arched backward, I have lost stamina and have wasted oxygen. So curl your body into a RELAXED FETAL POSITION. If your hands cannot clutch the bottom, use them to protect your head. Here we have a negative option. In high turbulence, even attempting the fetal position demands effort. But the trade-off is worth it.

When tossed about violently, you instinctively try to stabilize yourself. It frustrates and terrifies you to lose control of your body. You approach that perceived hopeless situation. Panic is about to flood your brain. One component in the counterintuitive passivity helps stave off panic. How?

My homespun solution is to COUNT SLOWLY AND EVENLY. In extreme turbulence I find it incredibly difficult to begin this simple cogitative function. But once started, I release my mind from the clutches of panic. Counting guides your jostled brain into thinking mode. It keeps thoughts from racing out of control. It is so simple: Just think slowly and calmly. The highest count I ever reached under a wave was nine seconds. That was an eternity, spiced up by not knowing when the count would end. Under-wave turbulence may have held me under even longer when I did not count. I hope never to break the nine-second record.

When the turbulence eases, pushing up from the bottom speeds you to the surface. Let us review and add a few refinements.

1. Big breath.
2. If possible get to the bottom.
3. Relaxed fetal position. Protect your head.

4. Do not struggle.
5. Count slowly and evenly.
6. When you surface take in air quickly.
7. Face the sea for the next wave.

Feel confident now? You had better not. These seven points are the best I can come up with after forty-plus years of experience. Do you recall my confidence in Chapter One, where I blithely provide a nearly 100 percent guarantee that an ocean lifeguard cannot drown in a rip? Well, all bets are off with under-wave turbulence.

Oh yes, there is one bet. It rests on good judgment. When the surf is monstrously roiled and dazzling (think introduction to Richard Rodgers's *Victory at Sea*), enjoy its wild beauty from the safety of the shore.

In turbulent surf, gird yourself for the unexpected. Surprises in big surf offer little margin for error. You cannot undo your mistake. And, well, potentially deadly surprises just plain scare me. You will see why with the following survival story.

Enter Hurricane Felix, a Category 4 tropical cyclone that hovered off the eastern seaboard for about a week in 1995, heaving huge swells shoreward. There I was, trying to ride waves in merciless surf. Twelve-foot waves were crashing on a sandbar only nine feet deep. Suddenly, a huge wave broke fifty feet beyond the other waves and raced toward me. Big waves are not only bigger, they are faster. At the last instant I barely dove under before the white water washed over me. I surfaced to face another white wall almost upon me. With lungs only half filled, I dove under. When I resurfaced, I felt unusually drained. I must have been struggling. A third wave bore down on me. It was not as big as the first two. I thought I had it made.

Facing seaward, I became aware of something behind me. As I glanced toward shore, a wall of water racing seaward bashed me in the face. Backwash—it was a wave actually rolling back out to sea. It rammed a huge gulp of water down my throat. I dove under the third wave with salt water in my stomach and no air in my lungs. Salt water is a poor alternative for air. Calmly, and with a curiously calm resignation, I ticked off nine seconds. I bobbed up to the surface. I had made it. Or so I thought.

Ah, the surface. Where could it be? There was no surface. Instead, my head wallowed in a meringue-like foam that was at least a foot thick. (The next time you eat a lemon meringue pie, imagine putting your face in the topping and trying to breathe. You may get egg white in your face but no air.) My only hope lay in somehow getting out beyond where the waves were breaking. There I could rest. I had spent nearly all my strength, and I sensed that another underwater session would be my last.

Then, for the third time in less than a minute, the ocean surprised me. The surface became eerily calm, the meringue began to dissipate, revealing in patches a softly undulating, glassy surface. With my remaining strength

I sprinted for the safety of deep water. There I rolled on my back, deeply sucking in air. Floating in that sudden stillness I thought how silly I would feel had I made a promise to the Great Creator that if I survive I would cede my earthly possessions to a leper colony and become a Trappist monk. I would have had to claim weakly that I made those promises under duress, and therefore they were invalid. Frankly, the only reason I made no plea was that I had no time to think of it.

Here is what did race through my brain under that last wave. I tumbled about feeling as if I were locked in a room the size of my body. As I slowly counted out those nine seconds, a thought occurred. I had often blustered about being dad-gummed if I was going to end my days in an assisted-living establishment, drooling on my bib, shuffling about in a rear-ventilated hospital gown. I did not think all those words. They formed the backdrop for my final thought, word for word: "Well, big fella, you got your wish." Then a deep calm filled me. In retrospect, yoga might have provided a safer way to achieve serenity.

As you take in all of this, you very well may be smirking: "If you are such a water expert, then why did you go into the surf when you knew it was so treacherous?"

My best answer is to smile engagingly, tap dance around that barb, and ask why a butcher shop is like the ocean. Because, oh perceptive reader, in both you can expect the wurst. In other words, for my blithe overconfidence, I have no excuse.

How About a Hand for Our Two Killers

The most common danger for the ocean bather is the rip. The rip is a current. It is limited in length and width. Somewhere offshore it eventually dissipates. It can strengthen, weaken, or cease to exist before your eyes. Most important, it does not pull you under. When you arm yourself with knowledge, the proper mind-set, and a strategy, the rip loses its killer status. When you control panic, your chances of survival soar.

Under-wave turbulence can kill. All the knowledge you possess; the calmest, most rational mind-set you can muster; and the most brilliant strategy can be useless. Get conked on your head or run out of air, and you will make a major donation to the ocean's food chain. And it is not tax deductible.

You make your best strategy on the beach. Assess the surf and decide whether you should go into the water.

This leads us to the key factor in survival. You. Here is what you bring to the survival formula: *knowledge of the water, a calm state of mind, and the capacity to form a strategy.* From my Hurricane Felix escapade, you can glean that good judgment, which clearly trumps overconfidence, is the key weapon in your arsenal of preparedness.

Learn to accept what the ocean is dishing out at a given time. Do not delude yourself that you can out-muscle the ocean. Acknowledge its power. Try to work around it. If that is not possible, stay out of the water.

During the Second World War, the Allied merchant marine fleet suffered horribly from Nazi U-boat attacks. Thousands of merchant seamen who survived the sinking of their ships perished after securing themselves on rafts and lifeboats.

"What do you expect? You are cold, wet, hungry, possibly injured, and in a lifeboat in the North Atlantic. It's not a Club Med getaway."

Here is a curious point. Tough young men were dying at a dramatically higher rate than their older and presumably less hardy shipmates.

For the older seamen, survival lay not in physical strength but in how they accepted reality and coped with crisis. The younger men instinctively resorted to physical strength. When it waned, they had no alternative source of strength. The older men somehow preserved precious inner resources. If this phenomenon of survival piques your interest, look up Outward Bound (www.outwardbound.org). This survival school developed its program on the experiences of World War II's survivors of U-boat attacks.[5] Here is a little tease from the Outward Bound website: it "help[s] individuals discover strengths they didn't know they had."[6] In a modest way

---

[5]"A Powerful Force for Good Since 1961," Outward Bound, *available at* http://www.outwardbound.org/about-outward-bound/outward-bound-today/history (last visited February 14, 2017).

[6]"Our Programs," Outward Bound, *available at* http://www.outwardbound.org/programs (last visited February 14, 2017).

we are attempting to do the same, as we learn about the ocean and about ourselves.

Knowledge is our goal. The path to disaster starts with ignorance and overconfidence. That goes for everyone out there, including me, when I ignore my own lessons. Ignorance, indifference, and overconfidence lead to STRUGGLE, FRUSTRATION, and finally to—let us all say it in unison—PANIC.

Chapter Five

The Tough Call—Do Not Go In

A Thousand Times No

Now we tackle a real burner. You ask, "Suppose someone else is in trouble in the water? With what I am learning about the ocean, why shouldn't I go in to help a bather in distress?"

My answer is NO, NO, NO, and again NO!

I can guess your response: "Mr. Expert, if you tell me never to assist a bather in trouble, then why not stop right here? Or do you intend to spend a whole chapter telling me *not* to rescue someone?"

Your question is reasonable. Undoubtedly you have noble sentiments about helping a fellow human being, and you probably have sound reasons as well. I suggest that we clarify them. Then, after reviewing your argument, let me present my case. I must warn you that it is filled with devils in the details.

I concede a few points that support your position. You have progressed beyond the demons in the ocean stage. You understand rips and what to do about them. By having pursued the subject this far, you show interest in—and perhaps an aptitude for—rescue work.

Aptitude rates higher than you may think. Let us be frank. High intelligence is not a requisite. One of my bright colleagues often lost his composure on rescues and rendered himself useless. As for piles of musculature, a few of my muscle-ripped colleagues were worthless lifeguards, despite their *Baywatch* personas. They were lax on watching bathers, could not anticipate problems, or spent too much time away from their post.

On the other hand, two of the finest lifeguards I know were smallish fellows. They could relax and at the same time concentrate on watching bathers. They anticipated trouble and carried out rescues competently. One of them was not the sharpest knife, et cetera, and the other had a congenital foot handicap that forced him to limp slightly. But they had aptitude.

I lob the ball into your court. Do you have the aptitude? Suppose that having entered a crisis situation, you flunk Aptitude 101? Should you fail, you may not be around to take a retest, if you catch my drift.

As for the hypothetical bather in trouble, let's add a few devilish details. The victim is ignorant of rips and does not understand what is causing the problem. Poor physical condition or a serious physical disorder, such as a weak heart, may be a factor. The victim may have panicked. Panicky folks are a drag. They tend to sink. Some may grab you. You assume the responsibility of keeping that person afloat and alive. Incidentally, you must remember to stay afloat yourself. Are you just a bit unnerved? No? Rats. You remain unconvinced.

Spare the Ethical Goo

You might want to split ethical hairs with me. "What about my moral obligation to help my fellow human being, my love of humanity?" You make a neat point, but you have an even stronger argument than that. (Why in the world am I giving you ammunition?)

Think of the loyalties of combat soldiers. While defending the flag is noble, their deep loyalty goes to their buddies—the people they know. Despite my best arguments against going to help someone in a rip, you may have a stronger motivation.

"That's right. Suppose that victim is not a stranger? Suppose it is my best friend, my girlfriend, or my child? I *have* to help, even if I risk my life."

You have read my mind. That's the motivation that scares me. You are willing to put your own life at serious risk. And guess what. Dead is dead, regardless of your altruism.

I concede that with this sticky ethical stuff, along with the personal element, you have lobbed the ball back into my court. I acknowledge your position, but I do not abandon mine. Under certain circumstances you would risk your safety to help a bather in distress. The thought of it sends a shudder up my spine. But you remain adamant. So let us see how you can best prepare to help another bather.

Heed this preliminary advice. NEVER try to help a professional when he or she is on a rescue. Okay, so it is your nephew Melvin. Yes, I know, you brought him to the beach and feel responsible for him. Still, I do not care how many patches, badges, certifications, or tattoos you may have or even that you have read Chapter Three of this book. The professional lifeguard neither wants nor needs your help.

I grant the statistical possibility—and it is a microscopic one—that a lifeguard may ask for help. This help would not directly involve you in the rescue. No lifeguard of sound mind would invite a bather into a rip that has already caught at least one victim. But say two lifeguards are on duty. They are watching about eight hundred bathers. A big rip has started. Twelve bathers are in trouble. Both lifeguards must go on the rescue. They must leave the other bathers unattended. Lifeguard posts may be far apart, without electronic communication, though this is increasingly rare. The guards might ask you to summon lifeguards from another beach or to call the first aid squad.

I appreciate zeal. But in my experience, well-intentioned amateurs only hindered the actual rescue—at best. At worst they became dangerous. As a rookie, I watched older lifeguards hastily and roughly shove aside would-be helpers. I learned why the hard way.

On some rescues the first lifeguard swims out with his buoy and secures the victim. At his signal, a second lifeguard swims out towing a line. On the beach a third rescuer receives a signal from the guards in the water and slowly pulls in the line. Caught up in the excitement, some onlookers zealously seize the rope and race up the beach with it.

In the abstract, community involvement sounds fine. Faster is generally better. The self-appointed helpers intuitively pull the line as fast as they can. Unfortunately, the opposite is true. *Slow* is better. The rescue line *must* move at a snail's pace. If not, both rescuer and victim can be towed to shore underwater. This is not good for the survival rate.

Such was my lot as uninvited volunteers towed a bather and me more than thirty yards underwater. My buddies finally wrenched the volunteers off the line. To keep us from drowning, I had to release the rescue line. Then my partner had to swim the line back out to us while other lifeguards kept volunteers at bay.

Here is another "Please do not help" story with a painful and nearly fatal lesson for the would-be rescuer. My wife and I were vacationing on Grand Cayman. We drove our rented motor scooter to various secluded beaches on the island, where we swam and snorkeled.

One day we found a lovely little beach. There was a gap in the reef, through which launches from ships could come to a concrete landing for supplies. While snorkeling in the gap, I noticed a strong rip pulling straight out. I strode out of the water about a hundred feet away from where I entered. A copse of trees stood between me and my point of entry.

Suddenly my wife called to me from the other side of the trees. "Ken, there's a man in trouble out there." I shouted for her to tell any would-be helpers to stay out of the water and that a professional lifeguard was on the scene.

I ran back to the concrete landing and jumped in. After about eighty yards, I reached the man. He still wore his mask, snorkel, and fins. He appeared to be in his late thirties or early forties, and weighed more than two hundred pounds.

To put him at ease, I said, "I am a professional lifeguard. We are floating nicely. The water is warm, so if we just relax, we'll get back to shore with no problem."

In a toneless voice he said, "I'm going to die." Then with a sudden dismissive motion, as if fed up with something, he ripped the mask from his forehead and slowly slid below the surface. With one hand I grabbed the back of his T-shirt, and with the palm of my other hand I raised his back, so that he floated on his back.

I wanted to restore his mental state to where he could respond to me. "Try to relax. Breathe slowly and evenly. If you can, just flick your fins slightly."

"I can't. My legs are cramping." A good sign though. He was responsive.

I towed him parallel to the shore as close to the reef as I dared go. Fortunately, next to the reef the current was weak. That meant we could avoid climbing onto the reef. We slowly made headway toward shore. Eventually, my feet touched bottom.

At this point, rescuer number two swam up, offering to help. I asked whether he had heard the lady on the dock warning people not to enter the water. He replied that he had his life-saving certificate and wanted to help.

Before I could reply with something—like a good lifesaver should follow orders—my wife again shouted to me from beyond the trees, "There's another guy out there!" Victim number two had also gone in to help. To keep the cast of characters straight, he was also rescuer number three.

I dared not leave the original victim. He was in shock. He might have had a weak heart. I placed him supine on the sand, telling him to rest there with his knees raised.

At this point the volunteer actually helped by staying with the victim. Then I ran through the trees back to the dock.

Near the landing I found victim number two, or the third would-be rescuer. A Caymanian had driven his truck onto the landing, cast a line, and towed him in over the barnacle-encrusted concrete. The poor fellow sat slumped against a tree, in a dazed state. A ghastly smear of blood and vomit slid down his chest. My wife had also advised him not to go in.

Why do nonprofessionals believe they can be useful on an ocean rescue? Who would dream of entering a blazing building to help a firefighter? Who would charge in to help a police officer at a shootout? Or a first aid squad at an auto accident? How about going into the kitchen of a restaurant to offer the chef a helping hand? (On certain occasions that might not be such a bad idea.)

You retort, "How about the Heimlich maneuver?" You just had to squeeze in that one. Well, the catch is that the Heimlich doesn't risk your own safety.

The would-be rescuers on Grand Cayman had allowed good intentions (similar to your noble sentiments and reasons), perhaps spiced with testosterone, to blur their judgment. They naïvely misread the danger in a seemingly harmless environment. They rushed into a situation that had taken me three years and more than three hundred rescues to feel fully vetted as a rescuer. This is why I discourage you.

"It is a strong argument," you say. "Suppose the victim's only chance of survival is with my help? Suppose that person is a loved one? I have little choice but to help."

Now for Those Devilish Little Details: Brace Yourself

With great reluctance I suggest the following steps. Do not take them in any way as *ipso facto* approval or encouragement of your attempt at rescue. Here goes: Assess the problem. If the bather is in good health and still cannot get to shore, the cause is likely a rip. How strong is the rip? If you helped the bather, could you both come straight in? Is the rip a screamer, requiring you to swim parallel to shore, and then in?

Do you absolutely have to go in alone? Could a human chain of available people reach the bather? Can the bather hear you and respond if you shout "Swim parallel to shore, and then come in?" The bather might think you are nuts. Perhaps the surf is smothering your words or the bather is unable to follow your instructions.

What is their condition? Is the bather still swimming? Panicking? A sign of panic is a body position that I (and perhaps no one else) call the crab position. The victim's hands are on the surface somewhat in front of the chest. Elbows are out to the side. Head is low in the water. The person is no longer capable of stroking. The crab position reflects exhaustion, defeat, and probably panic.

Is the rip easing up at all? (How is that for wishful thinking?) If the rip remains strong, then the situation is critical. You must act with purpose. That does not mean dashing about with blurring speed and correspondingly blurred thinking.

One of my lifeguard colleagues spotted a bather in distress about fifteen feet from shore and sixty feet down the beach from our post. He leaped from the stand, slipped the rescue line over his shoulder, and raced off diagonally toward the water. He ran past a child who was playing in the sand. The line somehow looped around the youngster's neck and dragged him down the beach as an unwilling participant in the rescue. The lifeguard did not have to race blindly, nor did he need a rescue line, as the bather was close to shore. His poor judgment resulted in serious abrasions to the child's neck. The bather easily got to shore. Okay, it's true: Some guys have no aptitude for their trade.

We have touched on two factors. First, ASSESS THE VICTIM. Second, ASSESS THE OCEAN. These you have done. Here is the third: ASSESS YOURSELF AND YOUR STRATEGY.

Stay calm. Do not rush. Pace yourself. Save energy. Have you gotten into a problem-solving mode? How are your physical condition and general health? If you cannot calm yourself, and you are subpar physically, stop this madness now.

Is a buoyant object—life preserver, water wings, surfboard, tire tube, body board—available? If none of the usual water toys are around, be resourceful. How about a spare tire from a nearby auto or a large piece of driftwood? To use a baseball metaphor, a flotation object improves you from a .230 into a .400 hitter. For you nonbaseball people, that means you have transformed yourself from chopped liver into filet mignon.

I remind you that a .400 hitter still fails 60 percent of the time.

Your response: "Now that I am a .400 hitter, how in the world do I use your precious flotation device? Boy, do I hate it when you use phony, official-sounding terminology. Let's just call this doodad a buoy."

Agreed. But I'll make a few suggestions about how to handle flotation objects—oops!—buoys. The hard buoys are hazards. Even in light surf they can become lethal weapons. A buoy can skim on a wave with stunning speed and slam into your head. Imagine getting hit by a baseball bat. And talk about the big hurt—surfboards have struck me seven times. Each whack made a painful memory imprint. Sheer carelessness caused five of those accidents.

The last time I victimized myself, I had just finished riding a beautiful wave. I flipped backward off the surfboard and lay in the water, savoring the moment. The board bobbed gently about ten feet out to sea. A thought began to form in my mind: "This could be dangerous if a wave came and...."

Before I completed the thought, a small wave picked up the surfboard and skimmed it along the surface—straight into my face. Result: a gash on the cheek, a black eye, and memorable pain.

You can avoid painful recollections. When entering or leaving the surf, keep your body between the surf and the buoy. NEVER get between the buoy and the shore. You have heard of a rock and a hard place. Substitute hard "floating object" and "shore."

Let's move along. You have swum beyond the shore break, and the buoy has not split your skull. You reach Melvin, the victim. Position the buoy between you and Melvin, allowing him to grasp it rather than you. *At all costs do not let the victim latch onto you.* If they are too weak, get behind the victim and place their arms over the object. With your chest against the victim's back, hold the buoy with both hands.

"Great. If I use both my arms to keep the victim on the object, how do I make headway—walk on water?"

Ah, grasshopper, you approach enlightenment. A rescue is harder and more complex than it appears from shore. Your priority is to keep the victim afloat. If you need both arms to secure the victim, you may have to rely on a frog kick or a flutter kick. Kicking can drain energy quickly. Be patient. It will take a while to reach shore. Do not rush. Although you may have time, you do not have boundless energy.

If you have swim fins, use them. Again, go slowly, and use them gently. If you are not familiar with fins, and you use them under stress, your calves will cramp. Even if you have experience with fins, excitement and overexertion can cause cramps.

Let us construct a harsher scenario. You have no buoy or fins. The victim is not responding to your calls or making headway and has slipped into the crab position. You dive in. (There is no lifeguard's spouse telling you to stay out.) Work on your rescue strategy.

Here's just a word about victim types. (No, I am not going to make you float on your back while I digress yet again.) There are papa bathers, mama bathers, and baby bathers. In my experience, women make good rescue subjects. They respond to instructions and do not panic as easily as men. When brought to shore, they recuperate more easily from the ordeal.

Children are tricky. You must reach them quickly. Little boys especially may not be very buoyant. With kids, you have fewer margins for error.

We men are the most pathetic. After all, we do have our pride. We struggle. We become exhausted. We panic. We cannot or will not follow instructions. We try to hide our fear. We fear embarrassment. We go into shock. Not all of us, of course, but we men tend to suffer more when rescued. Perhaps we succumb to the macho impulse to use force. Having failed that, we lose face.

But enough male-bashing psychology. It does remind me of a story—a digression on a digression. It is sad but illuminating.

One of my friends, Carl, was vacationing in Hawaii. The sea was gentle, but there was a short, insignificant little rip. He saw a couple about fifteen feet away. The husband called over to him, saying that his wife needed help. My buddy swam over to them and lightly supported the wife under her elbow. For some reason the husband swam off aimlessly. Carl repeatedly called him to swim back. The husband kept swimming. Carl was concerned, but the frightened wife begged him not to leave her. They watched as the woman's husband swam off to his death. Male victims can be their own worst enemies.

Shall We Return to the Melvin Saga?

Back to your rescue plan: You have entered the water. You swim with your head up to keep the victim in view.

"Will you stop using that word, *victim*? It's my fourteen-year-old nephew, not a chunk of lobster bait."

Okay. Your nephew has exhausted himself. He is helpless. As you approach, keep your eyes on him. Swim steadily and evenly. Do not sprint. When you are close, place your body at a 45-degree angle to him. Do not touch him unless it is necessary. It is not a good idea to hinder or immobilize a person who can still swim without assistance.

If Melvin needs help, hold him gently but firmly behind his closest elbow. This grip frees him to propel himself with his other arm and his feet. My approach here is a variant on Red Cross holds. They are aggressive and controlling, and we should use them only if needed. Let Melvin be as self-sufficient as possible.

This approach nearly ruined a promising friendship with the young lady who later became my wife. That's right: another anecdote. Humor me.

The story begins with a surfside spat. In a huff, she dives into the water and swims in the general direction of France. Realizing that she has forgotten her passport, he jumps in and, after swimming a hundred yards, he catches up with her. She is exhausted.

"Aren't you going to help me?" she gasps. "After all, you *are* a lifeguard."

He agrees and tells her to float on her back, rest, and breathe deeply. Eventually they reach shore.

"Some lifeguard. You didn't even help me."

"I did so. You're on the beach," he mumbles defensively.

"No, you didn't even touch me."

This from the woman that I would one day marry.

Back to Melvin. I hate to broach the subject, but are you certain this acne-challenged, sullen, post-pubescent urchin in the throes of teenopause is worth the trouble?

All right, I slap my wrist and press on.

If Melvin grabs at you, tighten your grip on his elbow (on the pressure point) and turn his body slightly *away* from you. You are also in a position to deflect him gently with your foot on his hip or knee. Congratulations. You have now joined your fate with Melvin's. But you are both afloat. That is the priority.

Allow me to digress yet again, for the last time—well, almost.

The Red Cross senior lifesaving course provides valuable information on breaking holds of victims. But in twenty-six years as a lifeguard and the dozen or so rescues I have made since retiring, I have never met an aggressive victim. (*Aggressive* and *victim* have been for me as incongruous as jumbo and shrimp.) Still, the possibility lurks that the next victim will use me as his personal buoy.

One of my colleagues recounted his rescue of three bathers. He followed protocol by placing the buoy between him and the trio. In a flash the only man, all two-hundred pounds of him, suddenly lunged on top of the buoy, nearly submerging it. Had there been no buoy between them, the man would have latched onto the lifeguard.

The rest of the rescue worked well. The man had frozen in place on the buoy. The other two bathers used him as a surrogate buoy while the lifeguards towed them to shore.

A woman friend, an experienced water person and powerful swimmer, told me this near tragedy. She swam out to a man who was calling for help. As she approached, she told him to stay calm and follow her example, specifically instructing him not to grab at her. As she drew near he flew at her and wrapped both arms around her neck. Both went under. Lifeguards got them in, but my friend required resuscitation.

That is why I recommend an oblique angle of approach, which allows you to deflect a person who lunges at you. Keep that lunge foremost in your mind as you approach. Push off forcefully and quickly. Politeness is unnecessary; your life may be at stake.

Red Cross rescue techniques are basic to a lifeguard's preparedness. Application of them would have kept my friend from nearly drowning. The next victim you approach could be a panicked sumo wrestler. Ponder that image: four hundred out-of-control pounds flopping on you.

Knowledge of breaks and holds makes sense and boosts confidence. Kudos also to the first aid, CPR, and automated external defibrillator (AED) training in the various Red Cross programs. In addition, I suggest the *American Red Cross Swimming and Water Safety Manual*[7] and the United States Lifesaving Association[8] as sound reference sources.

Doesn't all that a rescuer should know intimidate you just a bit?

---

[7]"Swimming and Water Safety" manual, *The American National Red Cross*, 2009, *available at* https://www.redcross.org/images/MEDIA_Custom ProductCatalog/m3240085_SwimmingWaterSafety.pdf (last visited February 14, 2017).

[8]http://www.usla.org.

You can't just read the manual, flip it on a shelf, kick back in your easy chair and say "Yup, I got it." Be warned. Much content in the Red Cross lifeguard training requires formal coursework to hone skills needed to deflect a strong, panicked, and desperate victim. You cannot afford to get it wrong. If you mess up, you could find yourself on the ocean floor with that sumo wrestler's arms wrapped around your neck.

Shall we return to Melvin? He is starting to sink. Struggle has exhausted him. Now you really must touch the little rascal. The Red Cross lifeguard training provides instruction for keeping victims afloat. Oh, you haven't taken the course? For now, here is a mini-lesson: With one hand under the person's chin and the other hand under his back, gently level off his torso on the surface. Due to the buoyancy of salt water, this is easier than you might expect.

If Melvin's hair is long, you can grab it and start towing. If he is wearing a shirt, you can hold it. The cross-chest carry gives you control and a better chance of keeping his head above water. But the carry makes it more challenging to propel yourself through the water.

Let's pause for a reality check. Leveling off the victim and the cross-chest carry are part of the hands-on Red Cross program. If you do not know those techniques, how do you proceed? To continue with our Melvin scenario, we will stretch what is probable and hypothesize that you at least have a mental image of these techniques.

You must keep the two of you afloat. Your legs are treading water for two people. You may be tiring. An adrenaline surge may help you combat fatigue, at least for a while. Keep your breathing controlled. Stop and rest while gently treading water. Remember that if you burn up all your energy you are useless.

Having gotten this far, you deserve credit. You have already saved your nephew. If his health at this point is good, you do not need to rush. Rest if you so desire. Keep trying to elicit a response from him. Remind him to breathe easily. Reassure him. All that remains is to get him and you to shore.

Assess your progress. You are both ALIVE! You know the problem and how to solve it. Now SWIM PARALLEL TO SHORE, THEN IN. You are on your way to shore.

Let's review your preparation for this rescue.

1. ASSESS THE PROBLEM. Nephew cannot come in. He is in a rip.
2. ASSESS THE VICTIM. (a) Is he able to swim? (b) Is he exhausted? (c) Has he panicked? (d) Is he conscious? (e) Is he breathing? For our exercise, we assume that he cannot swim, is exhausted, and frightened, but he is conscious and breathing. These would be the most typical conditions.
3. ASSESS YOURSELF. Are you calm and rational? Are you in at least fair physical condition? Do you have any serious health problems? Can you devise a

rescue plan? Are there any buoyant objects that you can use? Have you considered that you might risk exhaustion or cramps? Are you ready to take responsibility for someone's life in a hostile setting? Have you tried to contact help before you set out?

On paper this seems like a lot of stuff to process. But if you are calm, your brain will soon filter and distill a sensible strategy.

An amateur rescue requires sober thought. If you come up short on points 2 and 3, the odds increase that you will die in your rescue attempt. I still marvel at the physical and emotional pounding would-be rescuers have suffered, as well as the sad irony of their perishing. Disaster can easily strike the inexperienced rescuer. The amateur rescuer is an easy mark for disaster with all its little devils in the details. And I have yet to make my final point.

I Slap Down My Trump Card

From personal observation, amateur rescue attempts resulted in *100 percent failure*. Often the rescuer fared far worse than the distressed bather.

Citing that 100 percent failure rate, I feared that I was unfairly bolstering my argument by offering only my observations. I sifted through the archives of our local newspaper from 1885 to the present, looking for reports of successful amateur rescues. The following is an excerpt of the first article I popped up. The prestigious award presented to the rescuer drew my attention.

> In February 2002, Kenneth Wingler [was] awarded the Carnegie Medal [for heroism] by the Carnegie Fund Commission.
>
> On July 1, 2000, Wingler and Kevin H. House, 47 … worked together to successfully rescue two girls from drowning.... However, House collapsed in the water at the end of the successful rescue, suffering a heart attack. He could not be revived.[9]

I swear to you on the proverbial stack of bibles that I was as blindsided as you may have been. The famous award and loose definition of "successful" drew me in. As a shill at a carnival sideshow might put it, "Hey, come on, pal, only one out of the four died. After all, folks, that is a .750 batting average!"

I leave further research on amateur rescues to you, as my constitution is too delicate for the task.

Let us address preexisting physical problems. In a recent news report, a thirty-five-year-old mother died while rescuing her two-year-old son. She "checked in

---

[9]"Dover man called 'hero of civilization,'" *Asbury Park Press*, February 26, 2002, *available at* https://www.newspapers.com/newspage/144889489 (last visited February 14, 2017).

regularly with her doctor and had [her congenital heart condition] under control."[10] She ran the Boston Marathon twice and the Leadville Trail 100, a hundred mile trek through rugged Rocky Mountain terrain. Her son fell off a pontoon boat. He was not wearing a life preserver. The mom had to swim only a few feet. One may assume that emotional trauma triggered her heart failure. If you have a preexisting, potentially fatal health problem, even if it is "under control," you *must* disqualify yourself as a rescuer.

Good intentions and courage are not enough. *Courage that spawns poor judgment invites disaster.* Mark Twain would have expressed it less pompously, undoubtedly adding a pinch of humor. Okay. But consider the following newspaper report, which I only slightly abridged.

> *Location: Metropolis. City rescue team member spots woman teetering on railing of high suspension bridge. She leaps into river one hundred and eighty feet below. He hands cellular phone to bystander and leaps bravely after her. He hits water with same traumatic impact as she. Passing boat picks up the man and woman who recuperate together in hospital.*

That cellular phone might have summoned a rescue craft to the scene, thereby avoiding the risk of a second

---

[10]"Chelsey Russell, mother who drowned saving her child, overcame heart problems to become skilled athlete," *Denver Post*, August 26, 2016, *available at* http://www.denverpost.com/2016/08/26/chelsey-russell-athlete-mother-drowns-saving-child (last visited February 14, 2017).

life. Or someone else might have soared to the rescue. Metropolis? Hmm.

Knowledge, sound assessment, and proper planning improve chances of survival. This working thesis offers no guarantee. But it certainly beats risking your life in a poorly concocted display of courage.

Like the fellow who jumped off the bridge, you may ignore obvious danger and create a greater mess. I hope not. If you insist on trying to rescue your nephew, then what you have read here may tilt the odds a bit in your favor. But I hope the negative odds have sunk in. I have grown fond of Melvin. But remember that the story of his and your survival is merely hypothetical. The Melvin Rescue Saga, with its "devilish details," dramatizes the complex and daunting challenge a rescue attempt poses to nonprofessionals. In that spirit, may my words—DO NOT GO IN—continue to echo in your mind.

Chapter Six

Semper Paratus

The United States Coast Guard motto, *Semper Paratus*, "Always Ready,"[11] should characterize our relationship with the ocean. Despite our having locked horns with the folly of the amateur rescue, we agree on the value of preparation and prevention. It would have been far better if that nephew of yours could have avoided difficulty in the first place. *Preventicus est Betterus.*

Familiarize yourself with conditions at your beach. Where do rips typically develop? Do they shift or stay in one area? Can they become powerful enough to wash bathers away from shore? How far out do they flow? At what tide are they stronger? Watch for other hazards like sweeps and shore breaks. Do the waves become dangerously large?

---

[11]"SEMPER PARATUS: The Meaning," William R. Wells, II, 2006, *available at* https://www.uscg.mil/history/articles/SemperParatusTheMeaning.pdf (last visited February 14, 2017).

Share Your Knowledge

Help friends and loved ones spot rips. Tact is a consideration. Some rock 'em–sock 'em guys bridle at advice. It is much like the husband who could use driving directions but, ignoring his wife, stubbornly refuses to ask for directions. Testosterone-soaked egos react negatively to advice about the ocean, especially from other males.

Some people resent unpleasant news after having spent a bundle of money for a beach vacation. One summer I visited a picturesque East Coast resort. Unfortunately, this resort is nestled near the mouth of a highly polluted river. The metallic-appearing water set off alarms in my already abused sinuses.

While chatting with a vacationer who was there with his family, I alerted him to the poor water quality. He cut short our chat and walked away. It dawned on me that he did not need me to dampen his spirits, particularly with tainted ocean water.

I have learned to tread carefully when telling a bather about a rip. So far I have avoided—barely—that *Who asked you?* look. Even if your skills in diplomacy match mine, it is still worth informing bathers of potential danger, especially when no lifeguard is present.

Watch Those Kids!

Always, WITHOUT EXCEPTION, monitor your kids around water, be it ocean, pond, lake, stream, river, pool, or even bathtub. Backyard pool drownings far exceed accidental shooting fatalities. In 2009, unintentional drownings among children under 15 years old totaled 704. Shooting fatalities in the same age group were 223. That's a ratio of three to one![12] You cannot afford an attention lapse when your child is in or near water. Equally true, it is too risky to entrust your child to others, even professionals. Buoyancy devices such as tubes or water wings should never substitute for your alert presence. You are your child's best, and probably only, life preserver.

On a winter day I was swimming laps in a YMCA pool. I turned at the wall and swam toward the deep end, following the blue stripe on the bottom. Drawing even with the lifeguard on his high chair, I spotted a small child lying on the stripe. I dove and fetched him up. He could not have been lying on that stripe more

---

[12]"10 Leading Causes of Injury Deaths by Age Group Highlighting Violence-Related Injury Deaths, United States–2009," *Centers for Disease Control, available at* https://www.cdc.gov/injury/wisqars/pdf/leading_causes_injury_deaths_age_group_highlighting_violence-related-injury_deaths_us_2009-a.pdf (last visited February 14, 2017).

than about ten seconds. I handed him to the lifeguard who had frantically jumped in. Later, while showering, I reconstructed the scene. A parent was not present. The lifeguard responded only after I had brought the child to the surface. In short, two adults had failed their responsibility to that child.

Do not be lulled into a false sense of safety, even if your child can swim. In a rip, a child's journey to disaster accelerates. They might swallow water, gag, and suddenly become ill. Wave backwash can suddenly pull them out beyond their depth. You do not want your child to be the one that the lifeguard did not see slip under the surface while you were off buying refreshments. I can only imagine how often grief-stricken parents have lamented afterward, "I just left my child for a few seconds to get a [whatever]." They traded their child for a "whatever."

Even on the calmest of days I watched for kids bobbing about on floats or tubes. If no adult was in attendance, I had the kids show me how well they could swim. If they failed the test, I would bring them to their parents and suggest that they accompany their kids in the water.

Trust But Make Sure

It pains me to broach the subject, but the occasional inexperienced or, worse, incompetent lifeguard does exist.

Inexperience is understandable. What is risky is the rookie watching bathers without an experienced partner.

When you spot a rip, you will be able to check whether the lifeguard recognizes the trouble area. The ocean lifeguard has an advantage over his pool or lake counterpart, for whom there are no obvious danger cues. A rip is like a poker player tipping a hand. When a rip develops, the lifeguard should go on heightened alert—focusing on where problems will most likely occur. If the rip becomes too powerful, the lifeguard can guide bathers to a safer area. But lifeguards who cannot spot a rip or who are inattentive lose that advantage and, to be blunt, are worthless.

I have seen lifeguards blowing whistles at bathers for unclear reasons. To bathers, overused whistles create white noise. I recall one young lifeguard tooting his whistle incessantly while a rip flowed nearby, causing him no obvious concern. Because he was looking in the opposite direction, I had to assume that he did not recognize it. Who knows? Maybe he was so cool that his style was too subtle for me to discern. Still, I choose to watch my loved ones more closely.

Allow Me to Introduce Noisy Lady

Let's slow down and stow the tar and feathers. There is no need for a witch hunt. Try not to nitpick. You might see a lifeguard chatting with a member of the opposite sex. No problem. But an obvious cause for concern is a lifeguard's back that is frequently turned to the sea. A lifeguard can converse while he competently scans the bathing area. Eyes learn to connect independently to the brain's red-alert cell.

I speak from painful experience, having been victimized by a self-appointed water safety zealot. The setting was a sunny morning, before the crowd arrived. The water was lake smooth. A couple of kids were playing in the water directly in front of my stand. Ah, I thought, the serene joy of sitting by the ocean and actually getting paid for it.

Suddenly, somewhere behind me, a woman's voice exploded like that of a Wagnerian soprano.

"LIFEGUARD, LIFEGUARD, WATCH THOSE BATHERS. GO GET THOSE KIDS! GET THEM NOW. WATCH THOSE POOR CHILDREN!" I turned to see, as she marched down to the water's edge, my tormentress, whom I shall henceforth call "Noisy Lady." She brought to mind a hatchet on legs. The verbal barrage lasted a few minutes. She looked up the beach and exclaimed, "Thank God you are here, Captain! What would we do without you?" My captain walked up to her. She spoke to him for a few minutes in conspiratorial tones. He looked at the sand, nodding now and then.

The captain climbed up on my stand and sat next to me. With lips barely moving he explained that Noisy Lady had been following him for a few days. Probably having selected him as her alpha male, she had been belaboring lifeguards, while praising the captain as some kind of Olympian god. She had made me a collateral victim of her bizarre courting ritual, and our luckless captain the target of her charms.

I suggest two criteria to gain an impression of a lifeguard's competence. First, is the lifeguard *watching the bathers*? Simple observation suffices here. As we saw, watching bathers is automatic for a competent lifeguard. Even after many years away from the profession, I am uncomfortable with my back to the water.

Second, does the lifeguard appear able to *spot a rip*? This is harder to ascertain, and you must take care not to overshoot the mark like Noisy Lady or, worse, interfere with a lifeguard in the performance of his or her duty. That is a legal no-no.

Be concerned should bathers be in a rip, perhaps even having difficulty, and the lifeguard's attention is obviously elsewhere. If by temperament you are an alarmist, you might be tempted to race along the water's edge wildly waving a hastily commandeered towel as a banner and screaming, "THERE'S A RIP! THERE'S A RIP! RUN FOR YOUR LIVES! THE LIFEGUARD IS DOZING!"

I hope the episode starring Noisy Lady tempers your zeal. Instead, try calmly telling friends and relatives about the rip, as you monitor it.

Another problem pops up in mid to late August. With the start of fall semester and sports programs, lifeguard crews thin out. It may be necessary to hire inexperienced applicants to fill the rosters. Often there are no applicants, and some beaches go unprotected.

Then there is the "college kid" compared to the career lifeguard. Smaller beach clubs and resorts may hire undergraduates. They may receive inadequate training and on-the-job mentoring for a stint that will last three or four summers. By the time they get some seasoning, they enter the next phase in their lives.

Here is a case in point, as reported in my local newspaper. A mom and her eleven-year-old son were caught in a rip. Four lifeguards responded. They rescued the child. His mother drowned. One of the lifeguards explained that they saved the boy, but when they went for the mom, it was too late. What is wrong with this picture? Four guards go to one victim, and no one goes to the other? One lifeguard, even without a rescue buoy, is enough to secure a victim. It is simple. Get there quickly. Keep the victim afloat. These guards were alert. But their apparent inexperience and inadequate training resulted in a death.

By contrast, in some states water rescue has the status of a primary or secondary career. I do not dismiss the three-year lifeguard out of hand. But if I had to choose between lifeguards from the Sleepy Summertime Tanning and Beach Ball Club or the rescue crew from the County of Los Angeles, I would lean toward the latter.

When Toys Are Tools

Bring those buoyant water toys to the beach. You remember, from the previous chapter, the ones that turn you into a .400 hitter. If you bathe at an unprotected beach you might even consider a standard rescue buoy, one of those gaudy orange or chartreuse jobs with handles and a line to loop over your shoulder.

One of my friends regularly tows a buoy when he swims. Some beaches require swimmers to tow a rescue buoy. It is not a bad idea. Should you encounter small boat traffic, the buoy increases your visibility. When resting, you can simply loll about with it under your arms. It makes a nice hedge against unforeseen problems.

No, people will not tease you for being overly cautious. Think like Tom Sawyer. Having to whitewash a fence, he spun his perceived burden into a desirable game. In the spirit of spinning, the buoy can serve as an orthopedic neck rest. Its flashy color helps you spot your blanket on a crowded beach. But seriously, remember that in Chapter Five we saw how helpful a properly used buoy can be during a rescue.

Speaking of proper use of a buoy, I recall the aforementioned lifeguard television series, *Baywatch*, which featured a gaggle of buff West Coast lifeguards. I watched ten minutes of one episode, galvanized by the tension. A beautiful woman in a red, skin-tight bathing suit was splashing her luscious way out to a bather in distress. As per protocol, she towed her bright orange buoy.

So far so good. But what did she do when she reached the flailing victim? She offered him her magnificently sculpted arm. "The buoy, the buoy!" I wailed at the television. "Why did you tow it out? Get that thing between you and him. You want him to grab the buoy, not you!"

THE BUOY, NOT THE ARM!

As for the drama, I could not wait to watch the ensuing underwater wrestling match, with his arms wrapped around her neck, and her eyes bulging out of her head. But no, the script took a rosier path.

Not as showy and more readily available is a body, or "boogie," board. It is a fine water toy for beginners as well as for water people, and it is handy if you get into a jam. It should have a leash that attaches to your wrist or upper arm. Its plastic-covered foam body is less likely to bang you up. If you wear fins with the board, your safety quotient soars. And with the bodyboard, no one will call you a safety wuss. Boogie boards are just plain fun to have at the beach.

To interject a sobering thought, my DO NOT GO IN admonition against attempting to rescue a bather in distress still holds. But remember my little grannydote in Chapter One. You and your trusty boogie board could already be in the surf with other bathers when a rip develops. The situation offers too many variables to discuss specific options. I have seen a person on a mat overwhelmed by panicked bathers trying to clamber on. Remember, my concern is for *your* safety. Protect yourself first.

Think of the instructions attendants give on a commercial flight. Should oxygen masks drop, put yours on first before assisting others, including Melvin. If the bathers have not panicked, lead by example, as discussed in

Chapter Three. Create your own grannydote. But take great care to keep your distance.

This advice may strike you as cruel. But it is senseless to risk becoming one more person in need of rescue. What you have learned can help you. But when you try to assist others in distress, what you have learned for your own safety becomes a house of cards in a windstorm. So I repeat. Use your knowledge, but offer help from a safe distance.

Consider this inexpensive little doodad—a Coast Guard–approved whistle, one that functions when wet. Several types are available at mail-order houses that specialize in outdoor activities.

My mocking alter ego can no longer restrain itself: "First you advocate rescue buoys, and now Coast Guard–approved gimmicks. You must have a rescue tool fetish issue. Let me guess. Your walls drool with the pathetic memorabilia of a has-been. You have your crossed oars, team photos, cheesy little trophies, bottled sand, a tacky collage of crumpled zinc oxide tubes, clamshell ashtrays. And now whistles?"

Now hold on a minute. We all know that even the most trivial surf is noisy. A whistle could help you draw a surfer's attention to a struggling bather. How about trying to get the attention of that pesky nephew of yours?

You shout to him, "Melvin, you're in a rip! Swim to your right!" Hopeless. He hears nothing. Now try it my way. Your toot gets his attention. He looks back at you. Now you can signal by hand and arm gestures and, if you are really prepared, by prearranged whistle signals. That two or three bucks makes a good investment.

For further reading you might review the Resources section in the back of this book. The National Oceanic and Atmospheric Administration (NOAA) website features excellent information on rip currents; the American Red Cross website includes sections on water safety, pool safety, basic first aid, resuscitation techniques, and rescue training; and the United States Lifeguard Association (USLA) website features sections on public education, as well as training and certification. I recommend a personal favorite—in Hernando County, Florida, a student organization called Squirtle Squad Scholars. (I personally love that title.) In 2015 these precocious kids developed an instructional manual on rip currents. So a valuable addition to any health class curriculum would be a final unit in June that features my favorite: the manual on rips by the Squirtle Squad Scholars.

All of these sources offer their own angles on rips and water safety. I suggest that you peruse them.

A Flip Side to Paradise?

Here is an extra dimension to the *Preventicus est Betterus* theme: You can better prepare for your vacation in paradise. We are ready for rip currents and under-wave turbulence. But some of those exotic subtropical resorts might blindside us with a rosy sales pitch.

For example, there may be no lifeguards at your destination. Worse, you might receive bland assurances of A-plus, 100-percent-safe surf conditions.

One winter my wife and I were cozily ensconced in Las Cabinas Exquisitas on the Pacific Coast of Costa Rica. The owner, a pleasant American lady, lavishly praised Playa Hermosa, or "Beautiful Beach," assuring us of perfectly safe water there. We arrived at a dazzling mile-long crescent beach, with crystalline white sand, palms, huge shade trees—and rips. I saw rips to the left, rips to the right, rips in front, rips starting at the water's edge. The place seemed like one gigantic rip. To the uninitiated, the scene displayed The Great Deceiver at its best, with innocuous waves and inviting gin-clear water. I stood there in amazement, wondering whether I was seeing more rips than still water.

A local fellow who was sitting beneath a tree picnicking with his family told me that no one bathes at this beach. The locals had learned from tragic experience. As for my American *cabina* keeper, either The Great Deceiver had worked his magic on her or she was on a personal crusade to reduce Earth's population. It evoked a variation on the *Sweeney Todd* theme, where, after sending us to our doom, our lady from the *cabinas* would snatch up our belongings for herself.

Even if a resort does have lifeguards, their sense of urgency is not guaranteed. One of my old lifeguard buddies was vacationing at a famous Mexican resort. It was sunset. He was dressing to go out to dinner. Standing on the balcony and adjusting his collar, he gazed out over the ocean. Suddenly he spotted a woman struggling in a long rip, about to disappear around a distant point of land. He raced down to the beach, shedding shoes and shirt. There he saw the lifeguards savoring a preprandial libation.

The story ends well. Now sufficiently fueled, *los muchachos* raced off to the rescue. However, during his week there my buddy learned of two tourist drownings. Locals told him that they occur regularly. This type of information does not appear in travel ads.

My old lifeguard mentors, the ones who sat with me on the bench and taught me "the fine points," might think my buddy's urgent response a little precious. The rule of thumb was, and I quote, "Wait until you see 'em suckin' water before you get 'em. Then they'll be grateful. If you go too soon, they'll cuss you out." Privately I thought a cussing out would beat arriving too late. But at least my mentors, to my knowledge, did not drink margaritas on the job.

What can you do to protect yourself on a strange shore? You have already begun. You know things about the surf that elude most beachgoers. You know how to form a survival strategy for yourself in a crisis. Now we are forming a preventive strategy in selecting a vacation venue. Here is another caveat.

Do not assume that the water is gin clear everywhere in those warm seas. I recall staying at a French-speaking resort with the charming motto *Avec les pieds au mer* ("With your feet in the sea"). Sadly, as my wife and I were dipping our tootsies, we saw a nearby sewer drain.

Some vacation resort literature describes surf conditions. The very mention of surf suggests a targeting of surfers. That is wonderful if you surf. If you do not, it might raise concern for your family's safety. If possible, check at least two sources. You might, as I did, turn up something like the following description: *The most exciting surf is on the famous Salsa Brava.... If you lose it* [your board, your bathing suit, your sense of reason?] *you're liable to smash yourself and your board* [ah, the surfboard!] *on the reef.*

Wouldn't grandma just love this place? How about suggesting it for the stereotypical overbearing in-law? One might even finance the trip. A resort that boasts beaches with "exciting" surf probably offers rips or under-wave turbulence, rocks or reefs—features that are definitely not family friendly.

Can We Finally Have Some Fun?

"Please tell me when you're going to let me have some fun in the water! You've turned me from a happy, ignorant swine into a wise, unhappy Socrates. Can't you just point me toward the water and let me oink around in it?"

I can, with pleasure. Consider yourself a happy Socrates—the best of both worlds. You are better prepared. You have a grasp of ocean hazards near the shore. You understand the need for a calm, problem-solving mindset. You understand rips and how to deal with them. In lifeguard parlance, you "know the water." Finally, you see the value of preparedness, vigilance, and good judgment.

In the sun, sand, and surf we have one of the finest recreational packages that nature offers. No spin or hard sell is necessary.

Enjoy it all, and be safe.

Afterword

Lifeguard or Swineherd?
Thoughts on Beach Access and Use

Herd 'Em, I Say!

Occasionally, friends have asked, "You loved being a lifeguard. Why did you quit?"

Twenty-six summers is a long time. New challenges entered my life. That is part of my answer. Another part lies in how the profession had changed.

When I became a lifeguard, we used a water safety policy that I term *protective*. We blew the whistle largely to guide people away from rips or dangerous shore breaks. We let bathers enjoy the water as much as possible.

I later grew aware of a gradual shift in water safety management. I call it *restrictive*. Herd bathers together, preferably at a knee-high depth too shallow for them to swim in, even in calm water. The ideal environment has no bathers in the water at all. That way, no one can drown.

To apply this *restrictive* logic in larger contexts, automobiles would be banned because people die in car crashes, and electricity would be outlawed because it burns houses. Or childbirth would be forbidden because those children will eventually die. After all, if there is no birth, logically there can be no death. *Restrictive* logic denies bathers reasonable access to the ocean, presumably in the interest of safety.

On some beaches a lifeguard may be rebuked if he or she rescues someone. The policymaker reasons that the lifeguard let the problem arise in the first place. But more than one factor can put a bather in distress. Did a rip suddenly emerge? Did the bather suddenly become ill? Was alcohol involved? To blame the lifeguard without examining specifics is irrational.

What is wrong with safety first? Would you risk my safety for abstract principles?

I hope not. But for you, the bather, and actually for me as well, I question knee-jerk authoritarian control over my right of personal choice. I do not concede the latter automatically.

Consider this setting. I am in the Rocky Mountains and plan to hike at high altitudes. A ranger warns that strong winds and heavy clouds foreshadow dangerous weather. He advises me not to hike that day. I have two choices: heed the expert advice and stay off the mountain, or exercise my right to hike regardless of the consequences—even if that choice is ill advised.

"Aha!" you exclaim. "At last you show your true colors, you wild-eyed anarchist. I see you holed up in a remote mountain compound, oiling your AK-47 and concocting a self-rule manifesto. Have you declared your house a sovereign state, and elected yourself president for life? *Viva el Supremo!*"

While the catchy title does intrigue me, I am merely presenting different approaches to beach "policing," along with their respective benefits and consequences.

Little Red Lifeguard Suit and the Three Modes

I distinguish three basic modes of safety management. On one end rests the *laissez-faire* mode, on the other the *restrictive*, and between them the *protective* mode.

Each mode balances security and freedom differently. *Laissez-faire*, roughly translated as "Don't interfere," allows freedom with increased risk.

I recall an unnerving experience as a first-year guard. The older lifeguards decided to play Whistle Chicken. Everyone flipped their whistle off the stand. The first one to retrieve their whistle and blow it to alert a bather was "chicken." This was during a busy beach week. The thousand or so bathers before us gradually spread out past the limits of the bathing safety zone. To my rookie's eye, they seemed to be drifting toward the horizon. A rip began to develop, and I caved: I retrieved my whistle and blew it.

With their contemptible game, those lifeguards had inadvertently applied the *laissez-faire* principle of complete freedom. Regardless of the cause, be it irresponsible horseplay or official policy, the principle remains the same: Leave the bathers alone. Do not even warn them. If they have trouble, rescue them.

From a negative viewpoint, *laissez-faire* reflects a careless optimism, or even indifference, toward a bather's competence in the surf. Viewed more positively, it respects the bather's freedom of choice.

The *restrictive* mode, with its "Keep 'em out" mantra, considers all bathers equally incompetent. The purpose of this mode is to ensure that you cannot possibly drown, even at the cost of having fun in the surf. A comparative example is a biosphere, which may double your life expectancy. That's wonderful—if you want to spend your hundred-plus years in a glass bubble. In setting up the rough equivalent of a biosphere, the *restrictive* mode treats us all like five-year-old clones.

I have seen lifeguards with righteous dedication forbid bathers past hip depth, even with a flat ocean. At one beach I witnessed—and I do not embellish for effect—a supervisor shouting "Keep 'em at knee depth!"

Imagine: You spend a day at that beach and your bathing suit never gets wet, unless you take a walk on the wild side and dunk your fanny.

One of my old lifeguard buddies, who is anything but a scofflaw, told me this story. While vacationing at a famous seaside resort, he concocted the rebellious idea of taking a swim. The water was placid, and the area teemed with bathers standing at waist depth. To avoid bumping anyone, he swam just beyond the bathers and parallel to shore at—horrors!—the forbidden chest depth.

When he returned to shore, lifeguards and police accosted him. On the verge of arresting him, they asked why he ignored their whistles. He replied that his ears had filled with water and he could not hear. My buddy prudently did not ask them to point out the danger, because it had become clear to him that *he* was the danger. He had violated the *restrictive* golden rule: Thou shall not stray from the pen.

Ironically, the swineherd-like *restrictive* mode denies lifeguards the opportunity for rescue experience that is vital when The Great Deceiver springs a surprise. Before my devil's advocate can charge that I favor luring bathers into rips so that lifeguards can practice their rescue techniques, let me elaborate.

Lifeguards can compensate for limited experience by running frequent and rigorous simulated ocean rescues. If the simulations are not realistic, they will be about as effective as sparring with your paunchy Uncle Alfred as you train for a main event fight. Rescues are main events; there are no second chances.

In my last few years as a lifeguard, the captain often deemed the ocean too dangerous for bathing. He frequently gave orders to keep everyone out of the water. In the abstract, one sees no issue: A supervisor is acting in the interest of public safety. Now let us flesh in that abstraction with a true scenario as it affects real people, one that repeated itself too often.

On a hot July weekend, hordes of day-trippers brave two-hour stop-and-go traffic for a day at the beach. Enter the glitch: At 9:00 a.m. the captain inspects the surf, sees rips, and departs with the order "Keep the bathers out." By 11:00 a.m. the waves die down, and the rips disappear, leaving safe bathing conditions. But the order remains in place. If I allow bathing, I disobey my captain's directive. Should an improbable disaster occur, I am legally responsible. The captain's command made sense at 9:00 a.m. Two hours later, however, its irrelevance tarnishes a beach day for lots of people.

I began to wonder why the *restrictive* mode was gaining traction, and I came up with several theories. First, strict control of bathers reduces litigation: fewer rescues, fewer lawsuits. Second, as one beach director told me, if "close supervision" is not employed with large numbers of bathers, the lifeguards' effectiveness is diminished. Third, the *restrictive* mode, in its simplicity (me swineherd, you swine), takes less work. All that's required are lifeguards with whistles and police with summons books.

The disdain implicit here suggests a fourth possibility for the *restrictive* mode's rise in popularity. Beach administrators employ the *restrictive* mode because they can. From my observations, beaches where local residents comprise a negligible part of the bathing public—as at larger "touristy" destinations—the *restrictive* mode seems to prevail. At smaller resorts, "regulars" can more readily exert influence on beach management. Because they live in the area, local residents tend to know more about the water and are more inclined to chafe at being herded.

Legal setbacks have impeded the quest for open access to the ocean. In rejecting an appellate challenge by three surfers (State of New Jersey *v.* Oliver, Schmitt, and Morgan [1999][13]), the court referred to the definition of *bathing* as published in *Webster's II New College Dictionary* (1995): "[t]o become immersed in or as if in a liquid." By applying this definition in a blanket statement to any activity that involved "entering the water," the court upheld a municipal ordinance that denied access to the water.

The result? The court effectively gave *carte blanche* for the *restrictive* mode of protection by overlooking a generalized definition of *bathing.* Water safety authorities could now legally classify all people who recreate in the

---

[13]http://caselaw.findlaw.com/nj-superior-court-appellate-division/1404057.html (last visited February 14, 2017).

water as "bathers." Accordingly, Michael Phelps fits in the same category as a week-old infant receiving baptism. The gates to the pigpen are opened wide for *restrictive* herding.

The most damaging consequence of the lump-them-all-together definition is that it empowers officials who are ignorant of water safety practices to administer the "bathing" principle at will. It is too easy: If an individual

is spotted "immersed in a liquid," simply order that person out. The official's reason can be as fickle as "I just feel like it." Yet despite this one-size-fits-all stacking of the deck, there is a glimmer of hope.

For many years, the *restrictive* mode was gaining traction. One summer, during off-hours, authorities hung chains across some New Jersey beach entrances. They allowed swimming only during official bathing hours. Portions of the bathing community began urging more flexibility. Informed groups pressed for more relaxed access to the ocean.

Noteworthy among these enlightened and energetic organizations is the Surfrider Foundation. I recommend that you read the organization's mission statement (www.surfrider.org/mission). Despite the ham-fisted legal definition of *bathing* as immersion in liquid, these grass-roots organizations have helped to blunt the *restrictive* momentum.

Moving to the opposite end of the continuum, I cannot envision a manageable *laissez-faire* mode in heavily populated areas. However, given sensible adjustments, the *laissez-faire* mode can effectively maintain safety. For example, people may bathe at Waimea Bay on Oahu's North Shore, despite the monstrous thirty-plus-foot waves. Are those bathers suicidal? No. The lifeguard scans the horizon while bathers enjoy the surf. When he spots a set of gigantic waves approaching in the distance, he

Some ocean communities close their waters to all activity when lifeguards are not present.

sounds an alarm. The bathers exit the water. The killer waves thunder in, then crash and roll onto the sand. The surf calms down. At the lifeguard's "all clear" signal, the bathers reenter the water.

Well, my devil's advocate, does all this freedom chatter leave you lightheaded? Would you prefer me to protect you from yourself? Shall I drive you into a pen where you will be safe?

Kidding aside, you may reject the "Warn them and let them be" approach. But if you cede freedom to authority, how far should that authority extend? Should it treat everyone, regardless of age or competence in the water, as mentally and physically challenged? Must everyone stay at knee depth regardless of the surf conditions? Why should a policy that recognizes only the least-able common denominator deny another, more capable bather or water person his or her chance at fun?

Enter the *protective* mode, which balances security and freedom. If at the potentially deadly Waimea Bay people can safely enjoy the water, surely we can eliminate rigid herding practices anywhere, and certainly on placid days.

Flexible measures are possible when the ocean kicks up its heels. Relocate bathing areas away from rips or pounding shore breaks. Close beaches with treacherous surf, and concentrate lifeguards on safer beaches. Monitor children with special care, and let adults enjoy the water. The *protective* mode allows adaptability and, frankly, requires harder work than the *restrictive* mode. Lifeguards would be doing what the public is paying them to do: helping people enjoy the water with due attention their to safety.

Lock 'Em Up

I have skirted the pesky law enforcement matter long enough. Suppose that after I caution a bather not to enter a rip he ignores my warning and enters the surf? On my beach, the policy was to contact the police, who in turn could arrest the bather.

"You are too delicate with the bather's feelings. If he ignores you, just run him in."

Well, the bather's legal standing concerns me. Let's identify the basis of a lifeguard's "police" powers, specifically how they affect water safety, and view those powers through the eyes of comparable oversight occupations.

I knew a teacher who favored corporal punishment in public schools. He reasoned, "If you park illegally, the cop comes and gives you a ticket, right? The law breaker must pay a price." Right you are about a price, and wrong you are about which price! Let's apply his parking analogy more accurately. If you park illegally, the cop comes along and whacks you with his stick. Issue a summons, all right; tow the car, if necessary; but beat the owner? Now that is an *extrinsic* consequence.

In the Colorado Rockies, the principle of *intrinsic* consequence reflects policy. A skier or climber may reject a mountain rescue specialist's warning. Should that individual have a mishap in the mountains that requires extraction, EMT attention, transport, and hospital services, there are relevant consequences. The injured climber must pay for all the emergency services that would have been avoided had he heeded the caution. Even in this scenario my teacher friend might say "Hey, you want intrinsic? Let him die up there. That'll serve him right."

Where does this harsh logic go horribly wrong? It ignores the basic mission of mountain rescuers and lifeguards. It is to protect, not punish, people in their domains, be they hikers or bathers—even when they act irresponsibly.

Let's get back to the surf. Suppose at your crowded beach a gaggle of bathers follows the scofflaw into the rip.

The arrest card ensures that no one may prevent the lifeguard from performing his duty. Why didn't I remember that card when Noisy Lady ambushed me? Legal action in her case could have been a consideration. My attention to bathers was interrupted by her, as well as by the hypothetical "gaggle of bathers."

Well, if we can shelve my fixation on Noisy Lady for a moment, we have stumbled on a basic principle: Anyone, bather or otherwise, who diverts you from your job is subject to legal action.

That's legal principle Number One. Let's move on to Number Two, with a few illuminating scenarios. If a crushing storm surf, with its deadly under-wave turbulence, huge rips, and shore break, seems suicidal to enter, then I have to insist on compliance. But I have a neat escape hatch for the legal issue.

Presto! It's The Great Terrifier, the ultimate wordless convincer. During my twenty-six years lifeguarding, when the ocean bared its teeth in all its thundering fury, not one soul ever ventured into the water. I did not have to explain the obvious menace. Legality never entered the picture.

Yet there always seems to be an exception, and this example occurred in the early days of surfing on the East Coast. Frank, a Hawaiian surfer, was visiting our town. On a day of large, roiled surf, a dry nor'easter, Frank entered the water on a borrowed board and set up about eighty feet beyond a jetty. I would not call the surf impossible, but bathers were not allowed in because of strong rips. Frank would take off on a huge wave, and before crashing into the face of the jetty, he would adroitly swerve his board up and out of the wave, soaring into the air at the last instant. Local surfers can now replicate that performance. But for us at the time it was dazzling and unique.

Our captain spotted Frank's acrobatics and screamed, "What is that nut doing out there? I want him arrested!" We lifeguards finally calmed him down, and the hammer of the law did not come down on Frank. Anyone could see that with his extraordinary surf competence, Frank was an exception, an individual who clearly exposed the absurdity of the "one who immerses in a liquid" definition. Without endangering other bathers, or even ourselves, we could respect Frank's uniqueness.

"You're still beating around the bush. Suppose a bather other than a big wave surfer INSISTS on going in? You still bear responsibility for his safety."

Enter legal principle Number Two: the lifeguard's personal safety. Say the storm surf is so violent that a competent lifeguard could easily perish on a rescue in surf too wild for even the best water person (like Frank). It is appropriate to warn the bather of legal consequences.

Smelling victory, my devil's advocate now goes for my jugular: "Another lukewarm response. I knew it all along. You really want total self-determination. That's why you hedge on enforcement. Guess what: In your dreams!"

No. My dream is more modest. I would settle for a more flexible legal definition of *bather* than "one who immerses in a liquid." The final scenario shows how that flexibility can work.

Here is a far more typical setting: The ocean is serving up fairly large, well-shaped waves—challenging surf but not deadly. It's the surf that competent surfers, boogie boarders, and bodysurfers pray for. Lifeguards expect competence in this type of surf. If I know a boogie boarder or a bodysurfer is competent, then in they go.

A person I do not know may demand equal access. Or I may call in from the surf a person who seems to be having difficulties. I tell the person, "We have to be confident that you can meet the challenges. Loop this rescue line over your shoulder and swim it out two hundred feet through the surf. If you succeed, then into the surf you go."

Parenthetically, I never had to proceed with the test. Perhaps the rescue line intimidated them. Perhaps they feared humiliation if they failed. Or perhaps they

This sign at Ke'e Beach, Kauai, explains surf danger along with a willingness to discuss access, probably based on a would-be bather's experience and physical ability. Photograph by Jack Hoban.

responded sensibly to their own reality check. Whatever their reasons, by offering options, I acted on the premise that all bathers are not the same.

The enforcement card has a place in a lifeguard's deck. It should be dealt only when needed to maintain the lifeguard's vigilance and his own safety. With its flexibility in daily on-the-scene problem solving, the *protective* mode effectively creates a reasonable balance of safety and freedom.

This inside peek at beach management has hopefully given you a better idea of how lifeguards ensure your safety. In a nutshell, if you surf big waves, you would prefer the *laissez-faire* mode—perhaps with common sense alerts in place, as at Waimea Bay. Or, if you need security, you might opt for the *restrictive* mode. Alternatives to its implied livestock management do exist, as the *protective* mode suggests.

When planning a beach or resort vacation, take the time to apply these criteria when making your choices. Whenever possible, check on surf access rules to avoid disappointment. If you live in a coastal community, use these criteria to better assess local water-safety management, as you can air your views with greater knowledge and confidence. After all, it is your ocean, too.

Glossary of Ocean-Related Terms Used in This Book

along-shore sweep a current that moves parallel to shore

backwash wave water that has run up the beach and then recedes or washes back to the ocean; also called *backrush*

bather 1. one who recreates in the ocean without particular knowledge of the surf; 2. legal definition: "one who immerses in a liquid"

berm a ridge of sand parallel to the water line

big wave surfing surfing waves of 20 feet or greater in height

bodyboard a foam board roughly 3 to 4 feet long by 20 inches wide for riding waves; also called *belly board* or *boogie board*

buoy a flotation device usually related to swimming or boating safety

caught inside   surfing term for an undesirable position: between the wave break and land

cliff diving   diving into water from a cliff; Acapulco, Mexico, is a world-famous location

comber   a huge wave

crab position   a bather's position, with hands in front of chest, elbows to side, and head low in water, suggesting exhaustion and possibly panic

crunch zone   area at the edge of the beach where waves break (*see also* shore break)

cut   a gap between a jetty and the beach or in a breakwater

ebb tide   the portion of time between high tide and low tide, when water flows away from shore

groin   a strong but short rip current close to shore

jetty   a man-made projection into the ocean, designed to control the movement of sand or to modify an along-shore current

laissez-faire   French expression roughly meaning "Don't interfere"

leeward where the wind blows *away* from the point of reference; for example, the side of a boat away from which the wind is blowing is the leeward side of the boat (*see also* windward)

life preserver a wearable flotation device

ocean lifeguard a lifeguard with knowledge of surf dynamics

protective mode *see* Afterword

rescue strategy *see* Chapter Five

restrictive mode *see* Afterword

rip lifeguard jargon for *rip current*

rip current an ocean current that generally flows away from shore

rip tide an incorrect variant of *rip current*, if used to describe an ocean condition

sandbar a shallow area in the water composed of sand

seaward toward the sea

sepus a Native American term for *tide* or *current*

set   a series of waves as they approach shore

shore break   a wave that breaks on or near land

shoreward   toward the shore

surf mat   an inflatable rubber or canvas device roughly three feet long by two feet wide for riding waves; also called *surf raft* or *raft*

surfboard   long, narrow flotation device for riding waves

swells   waves in deeper water, before they break

swim fins   rubber flippers worn on the feet

The Great Deceiver   the ocean as seducer, appearing calm and inviting

The Great Terrifier   the ocean as, well, terrifier—with large, thundering waves

tire tube   a potential flotation device

torp   localized lifeguard jargon for *torpedo buoy*

treading water   method of keeping one's head above water through gentle but steady arm and leg movements

troughs   areas between swells

under-wave turbulence   water turbulence beneath crashed waves

undertow a discredited, obsolete term that has incorrectly been used to describe a rip current, under-wave turbulence, or other ocean phenomena; incorrect when used in literal meaning

water person here, a person knowledgeable about the surf and its dangers

water wings an obsolete child's flotation device

whitecaps wind-driven froth on the tops of waves

windward where the wind blows *toward* the point of reference; for example, the side of the boat toward which the wind is blowing is the windward side of the boat (*see also* leeward)

Resources

American Red Cross
www.redcross.org

National Drowning Prevention Alliance (NDPA)
www.ndpa.org

National Oceanic and Atmospheric Administration (NOAA)
www.ripcurrents.noaa.gov

Outward Bound
www.outwardbound.org

Safer 3 Water Safety Foundation
www.safer3.org

Squirtle Squad
www.dep.state.fl.us/cmp/publications/cc/Squirtles.pdf

Surfrider Foundation
www.surfrider.org

United States Lifesaving Association (USLA)
www.usla.org

The author with his back to the ocean—a rare pose.

About the Author

Ken Cassie worked twenty-six summers as a lifeguard on beaches in Belmar, New Jersey. He studied at Cooper Union, Montclair University, Indiana University, Columbia University, and New York University, where he received a Ph.D. in Russian studies.

During the off-season he taught Russian, art, photography, and humanities. Ken served two tours with the United States Information Agency in the former Soviet Union, where he promoted American arts and culture in gallery and arena settings.

After retiring from both lifeguarding and teaching, Ken and his wife, Shelley, opened a pottery studio, Studio 103.

An avid water person, Ken enjoys swimming, riding waves, and paddling. Although retired as a lifeguard, he cannot change one deeply ingrained habit: On the beach he feels at ease only when facing the ocean, where he can observe water conditions and bathers.

CPSIA information can be obtained
at www.ICGtesting.com
Printed in the USA
LVOW12s0546060717

540418LV00002B/303/P